D1270631

The Cream of
Noël Coward

Selected by MICHAEL COX

Illustrated by HELEN SMITHSON

Preface by GRAHAM PAYN
& SHERIDAN MORLEY

The Folio Society
LONDON
1996

This edition is published by arrangement with the
Estate of Nöel Coward and Methuen London.

Copyright in all the Noël Coward material is by
the Estate of Noël Coward.

Introduction, selection and editorial matter
© The Folio Society Ltd 1996

Preface © Graham Payn and Sheridan Morley 1996

Illustrations © Helen Smithson 1996

Set in Dante with Gill Sans Extra Condensed
at The Folio Society.
Printed on Hamilton Wove paper
by St Edmundsbury Press, Bury St Edmunds.
Bound by Hunter & Foulis, Edinburgh.

Contents

Illustrations

Preface

There was not very much for me to do in *Words and Music*. Wearing a white jacket, shorts and top hat, I announced 'Mad Dogs'. I was also the beggar boy singing to a cinema queue as the lead-in to one of the show's biggest hits, 'Mad About the Boy'. Never had a young busker given such full value to his audience. I must have come across as a miniature whirling dervish. Pretty impressive stuff, I thought, until after a few rehearsals Noël came up and wagged his finger at me, the first of many thousands of times.

'Graham,' he said, '*we* know what a good little artist you are, but this boy, the character you're playing, *he* wouldn't know what you know. He'd stand quite still and *sing*.'

That was how I first met Noël Coward. It was 1932 and I was fourteen. I didn't really see him again until the war broke out: I remember him coming backstage after a performance of *Up and Doing* and being very nervous, not having seen him for the best part of ten years. From then on he kept a sometimes astringent eye on my career and, in 1945, offered me a role in his new revue, *Sigh no More*. It marked the beginning of a personal and professional relationship that would last until his death.

Both those songs from *Words and Music* – 'Mad Dogs and Englishmen' and 'Mad About the Boy' – were huge hits. There's often been speculation about who the original 'Boy' was. There's a school that puts its money on Rudolph Valentino, even though he'd been dead for a few years by the time the song was written. The lyric compares the 'Boy' to Ronald Colman, John Barrymore, Douglas Fairbanks, Jr., Gary Cooper, Ramon Novarro and Richard Dix, so they are all non-starters.

Sorry to disappoint the historians, but the 'Boy' was just an idealised version of every woman's fantasy and not based on anyone specific, but in excavating the truth I turned up an extraordinary 'lost' verse to the song, which I am happy to see included in this anthology.

This collection is a tribute to a legendary talent: too legendary, one might say. When William Fairchild, the script writer for

Star!, nervously showed Noël the part of the script that portrayed him and asked for his opinion, Noël answered, dead-pan: 'Too many "Dear Boys", dear boy.' The silk dressing-gowned figure with the cigarette holder, the clenched smile and the perennial talent to amuse has always been slightly at odds with the reality. When Sheridan Morley began to write the first biography of Coward more than twenty years ago he somehow imagined him born into a wealthy London family – Mayfair, possibly, or at worst, Belgravia. No such luck: 'I was born in Teddington, Middlesex, an ordinary middle-class little boy. I was not gutter. I did not gnaw kippers' heads on the pavement as Gertrude Lawrence always quite untruthfully insisted that she did. But nor was my first memory the crunch of carriage wheels in the drive, because we hadn't got a drive.'

It was early in 1910 that Mrs Coward's already ambitious eye fell on an advertisement in the *Daily Mirror* announcing the search for 'talented boy with attractive appearance' to appear in an all-children production of *The Goldfish* by Lila Field: she replied at once. Noël got the audition, and was told that he could play Prince Mussel for a fee of one-and-a-half guineas a week. There was a pause, after which Mrs Coward murmured that she couldn't afford it. Miss Field laughed politely, then explained that it was she who would be paying, and Noël got his first job.

By the beginning of the 1920s, songs and sketches and even full-length comedies were pouring out of him, and one was even staged, in London, just before his twenty-first birthday. It had little success but created a minor story for the gossip columns. 'There is something Puck-like about London's youngest dramatist,' wrote the *Daily Dispatch*, 'about the narrow slant of his grey-green eyes, the sleek backward rush of his hair. He is lithe as a fawn, and if you told him he was one of the three best dancers in town his grieved surprise at hearing of the other two would be only matched by his incredulity.'

It was not, he knew, quite enough to be a local boy from Teddington made good. Audiences of his early days required a kind of elegant, drawling, aristocratic glamour that did not go easily with his quick-fire, nervy delivery on stage. Nor did the content of these early songs seem totally in tune with the times: 'Dance

Little Lady' and 'Poor Little Rich Girl' are not, in fact, celebrations of 1920s hedonism, but strict moral warnings from the wrong side of the tracks about what happens in the world of cocktails and laughter. Noël was already more puritan, more dedicated to the Victorian value of hard work than was readily apparent from the carefree image he gave to press interviewers. One evening in a night-club he chanced to meet a friend – one with a mother inclined to pick up escorts still more youthful than her son. Here, he decided, was the beginning of a play: it was called *The Vortex* and it turned him into Shaftesbury Avenue's first angry young man.

In the long run, however, his greatest claim to theatrical permanence was to lie not with themes of sex and drugs, nor with the epic patriotic sweep of *Cavalcade*, nor with the pithy wit and musical brilliance of his various revues, but with romantic comedy, of which the greatest is undoubtedly *Private Lives* – included here in its entirety. It is the play which deals best with the perennial Coward situation of two people unable to live apart and, equally heartbreakingly, unable to live together.

The early 1950s were a bad time for him. The world that he had stood for as chronicler and critic, the world of the Bright Young Things, had been blasted to extinction by the Second World War. His manager Charles Cochran and his beloved Gertie Lawrence were both dead. He felt distanced and out of touch with England. But when the cabaret season got under way in the Coronation summer, a whole new audience came to find him at the Café de Paris. He looked in cabaret, said one critic, 'like a cardinal suddenly asked to participate in some frenetic tribal rite'. To use his own words, he 'tore the place up'.

It was the beginning of a Renaissance. As the critical wheel came full circle Coward assumed the role of grand old man of British drama. 'It's terrifying how little time there is left,' he wrote. 'Every day is now a dividend and there is so much I want to do.' His seventieth birthday in 1969 was marked by a week-long celebration on stage, screen and television, irreverently dubbed 'Holy Week' by Noël himself, and crowned by the news that he had at last been given the knighthood he deserved. 'I fear I shall not be there for lunch,' wrote his old friend the Queen

Mother, 'but perhaps you wouldn't mind making do with my daughters?'

Four years later he was dead. 'Some day, I suspect,' wrote Noël in his *Diaries* in 1956, 'when Jesus has definitely got me for a sunbeam, my works may be adequately assessed.'

This book is not an assessment: rather it is a celebration of Coward's generosity, over five decades, to his audience and a triumphant vindication of his own dictum:

Consider the public. Treat it with tact and courtesy. It will accept much from you if you are clever enough to win it to your side. Never fear it nor despise it. Coax it, charm it, interest it, stimulate it, shock it now and then if you must, make it laugh, make it cry and make it think, but above all, dear pioneers, in spite of indiscriminate and largely ignorant critical acclaim, in spite of awards and prizes and other dubious accolades, never never never bore the living hell out of it.

He didn't.

GRAHAM PAYN *and* SHERIDAN MORLEY

Introduction

Whenever his name is mentioned, the image of Noël Coward which springs into my mind is from the cover of the record of his Las Vegas cabaret appearances. He is, of course, in dinner jacket and black tie, standing alone with the great expanse of the Nevada desert behind him. For once he is without a cigarette; instead he is holding a cup of tea. It is a picture of the quintessential Englishman, keeping up the most impeccable of appearances, discreetly flying the flag – and, however alien the environment, rising above it.

This was not a character he created; it had grown naturally around him. He was born into the English middle class and would probably have remained an unremarkable member of it but for the fact that he had an extraordinary talent. Because it is a convenient quotation from one of his songs, it was often described as 'a talent to amuse' and it certainly gave him a childhood very different from that of his contemporaries. He made his first stage appearance at the age of seven and won his first paid engagement when he was ten, in *The Goldfish*, 'a fairy play with a star cast of wonder children'. Before he was very much older he was working with Sir Charles Hawtrey, who became his theatrical hero. When he was thirteen he first played Slightly in *Peter Pan* and, as Kenneth Tynan said many years later, 'you might say that he has been wholly in *Peter Pan* ever since'.

Early success must have played havoc with his formal education. As a professional child actor he was allowed two days off every week to look for work; frequently he found it, and that interrupted the process even more. With a mixture of pride and despair his mother once wrote, 'Noël did get some schooling in during 1912 . . .' One might have expected him to grow up without any literary background at all, but he was in fact profoundly well read. His work is enlivened by the most adroit use of quotation, and not just quotation from the Bible and Shakespeare, which most of his generation knew better than we do: a casual trawl through the Collected Lyrics produces phrases from

Byron, Keats and Shelley, Ernest Dowson, George Herbert, Disraeli, Swinburne, Burns and Yeats, all gracefully moulded to his purpose. He must have been a prodigious reader.

Of course, he had a skill with words, the ability to make them dance for him, which he was born with because it cannot be learned. The same was true of his musical talent. Here is a man who produced some of the loveliest melodies of the century, as well as film scores and a ballet, but could neither write nor read music. He enjoyed all sorts of popular song and could play the piano adequately – most often in the key of E flat. His taste in classical music was limited, however. A typical diary entry reads, 'Dined with Guthrie and went to *Così Fan Tutte* at the Met. Alfred Lunt's production brilliant but I hate Mozart, and I loathed the libretto.' In his autobiography there is a very funny description of his meeting with Sibelius in 1939. There was an insuperable language barrier between them, but the two composers had absolutely nothing to say to each other anyway.

It is not necessary to be musically educated to write great popular music. Jerome Kern *was* a music student, but George Gershwin only studied music *after* his early success and Irving Berlin had no musical education at all. These men, together with Cole Porter and Richard Rodgers, were the giants of American song in the first half of the century. There was only one Englishman who could be mentioned in the same breath and that was Noël Coward. And only two of them – Coward and Porter – had an equal facility in both words and music.

He wrote songs of every kind, but most of them fall into four distinct categories. There are the romantic songs like 'I'll See You Again' and the sheer fun of 'Mad Dogs and Englishmen' or 'The Stately Homes of England'. Then there are songs of social comment like 'Could You Please Oblige Us With a Bren Gun?' and 'Don't Make Fun of the Fair' which are almost historical documents. Perhaps most characteristic of all are the songs which evoke a period – 'Poor Little Rich Girl' for instance, a few bars of which conjures up the Jazz Age quite infallibly.

The songs, however, were only the beginning. In the middle of the Twenties, a decade which he invented almost single-handedly, he found sudden fame as a playwright. The first night

16

of *The Vortex*, which he also directed and played the lead in, belongs to theatrical legend. When the play was published Coward wrote, 'With this success came many pleasurable trappings. A car. New suits. Silk shirts. An extravagant amount of pyjamas and dressing-gowns, and a still more extravagant amount of publicity. I was photographed, and interviewed, and photographed again . . . on one occasion, sitting up in an over-elaborate bed looking like a heavily doped Chinese illusionist.' He blamed this photograph for all the allusions to decadence, cocktails and moral degeneration which were then applied to him, but had to admit that they were terribly good for business.

The Vortex has often been compared to *Look Back in Anger* because it is a cry of pain from disaffected youth. But it did not change the shape of the theatre as Osborne's play did, and Coward never wrote another play like it. The plays that followed, *Hay Fever* and *Fallen Angels*, were light comedies, and thirty years later Coward was still enjoying huge success in that tradition. But then again, this is not the whole of the story . . .

One of the aims of this collection is to show the diversity of Coward's talent. Over a working life of more than fifty years he wrote some thirty plays, a dozen musicals and revues, published two volumes of autobiography, four collections of short stories, one novel and a book of verse. He chose to preserve only about three hundred of his song lyrics, although he probably wrote twice as many. Altogether this is a body of work as large as Somerset Maugham's, much larger and more varied than Oscar Wilde's.

The amount he achieved in those years is amazing enough; the concentration of energy necessary to sustain it is extraordinary too. In his twenties he could appear in one of his own plays, while at the same time writing and composing a revue and seeing it into production. At one point he had four of his own stage works running in London simultaneously. In his fifties his stamina was undiminished: while directing Gladys Cooper in his play *Relative Values*, he was appearing in cabaret at the Café de Paris and writing *Quadrille* for Alfred Lunt and Lynn Fontanne. He also found time to work for the Actors' Orphanage, of which he was a very active President for twenty-two years. Given the quality of his work, this was more than just talent – it amounted to genius.

Allied to this enormous industry was his finely-turned sense of precision. You can hear it in that frequently imitated diction where every consonant is razor-sharp and every vowel has its proper value. In the Fifties this allowed him to take an old favourite like 'Mad Dogs and Englishmen' and turn it into a virtuoso display piece, delivered at a punishing speed with brilliant rubato. Not only is every word as clear and bright as a new penny, but that rattling pace increases the fun. Much earlier, in 1930, he recorded two scenes from *Private Lives* with the actress who inspired so much of his best work, Gertrude Lawrence. Here again is an example of dazzling technique which not only serves the writing but becomes part of it, so that you cannot imagine the lines being played in any other way. Although they appeared together relatively seldom and their performances were not preserved on film, this was a dazzling partnership. It is the vocal equivalent of the marvellous mayhem of Laurel and Hardy or the perfect balance of Fred Astaire and Ginger Rogers.

Those scenes, whether on the page or in performance, also demonstrate Coward's unerring ability to move us to tears with the simplest words. Although a writer who was a byword for sophistication, he had the most sympathetic understanding of the human heart and the loyalties and losses which break it. Which of us, man or woman, can read some of the scenes from *Cavalcade* or *This Happy Breed* without a lump in the throat? He described *Brief Encounter* very simply as 'the story of two ordinary people who met by chance, fell in love, and parted'. The setting is modern and suburban, but the rules by which those people live are as strict as those which govern a medieval Romance – and the pain is as intense. I doubt if there has been a better love story written this century.

Coward suggested that his own epitaph might be: 'He was much loved because he made people laugh and cry.' This is the simple truth, and we certainly remember the laughter before the tears. Each of us has a favourite Noël Coward story which sustains his reputation as a wit. One imperishable moment occurred during the Coronation in 1953 when the very substantial Queen of Tonga braved the rain in an open carriage accompanied by His Highness the Sultan of Kelantan. 'I wonder who that is beside her,' someone asked and Coward immediately replied, 'Her lunch!' Looking out of a window with a group of friends on another occasion, a small child spotted two dogs copulating and enquired what they were doing. Coward had an explanation ready. 'The dog in front is blind,' he said, 'and the one behind is very kindly pushing it towards St Dunstan's.'

He thoroughly enjoyed correspondence and the opportunity to send his enormous good humour winging round the world. When T. E. Lawrence wrote about his experiences in the R A F he sent a copy to Coward. The author's identity was disguised under his service number and an assumed name, 338171 A/C Shaw. Coward's reply began, 'Dear 338171 (may I call you 338?)'. Perhaps his most elegant message of all was the one he sent to Gertrude Lawrence on the occasion of her marriage to Richard Aldrich:

Dear Mrs A., Hooray, Hooray,
At last you are deflowered.
On this, as every other day,
I love you. Noël Coward.

With immaculate timing and the greatest good taste, it arrived on the morning after her wedding.

One might say that Coward, like Falstaff, was not only witty in himself 'but the cause that wit is in other men'. Graham Payn, his companion of many years, records a charming compliment paid to him by Alec Guinness on the award of Coward's knighthood in 1970 for services to the arts. For a man who had done so much, not only for the arts, but for human happiness in a wider definition, the honour came scandalously late. He was almost the last of his generation to become a theatrical knight: Olivier, Richardson, Gielgud, Redgrave and Guinness himself were all honoured before he was. Sir Alec wrote to congratulate him, saying, 'We have been like a row of teeth with a front tooth missing. Now we can smile again.'

At a time when elegance has almost completely disappeared

from public life, his contribution to the twentieth century seems more valuable than ever. We know that he stood for the old values, not simply dressing for dinner or helping old ladies across the road, but for dignity, decency, courtesy and generosity in every walk of life.

Towards the end of his life the Gillette razor blade company requested from him – and paid a lot of money for – a list of those things which he believed still had 'style'. The list ran:

A candy-striped jeep
Jane Austen
Cassius Clay
The Times before it changed
Danny La Rue
Charleston, South Carolina
'Monsieur' de Givenchy
A zebra (but *not* a zebra crossing)
Evading boredom
Gertrude Lawrence
The Paris Opera House
White
A seagull
A Brixham trawler
Margot Fonteyn
Any Cole Porter song
English pageantry
Marlene's voice
Lingfield has a tiny bit.

Of course, if anyone else of such discernment had been asked to write the list, Noël Coward's name would have been very near the top of it.

MICHAEL COX

A Note on the Text

This anthology is linked together, for the most part, by extracts from Noël Coward's autobiographies and diaries. *Present Indicative, Future Indefinite* and the uncompleted *Past Conditional* are now published in one volume as *The Autobiography of Noël Coward*. All the first-person reminiscences are taken from that collection except those from the *Diaries*, which are distinguished by a specific date. Other sources are identified in the text.

Where lyrics were attached to a specific show or revue, this has been noted in the contents list. Often they were not, and readers will find any background history in the book itself. The contents list also gives the sources of the selected poems and stories.

The Early Years

Noël Coward was born in Teddington, Middlesex on 16 December 1899.
He was the second son of respectable, hard-working, but certainly not
wealthy parents.

Oh, how fortunate I was to have been born poor. If Mother had
been able to afford to send me to private school, Eton and
Oxford or Cambridge, it would have probably set me back years.
I have always distrusted too much education and intellectualism;
it seems to me that they are always dead wrong about things that
really matter, however right they may be in their literary and
artistic assessments. There is something to me both arid and
damp about dwelling too much among the literary shades of the
past. My good fortune was to have a bright, acquisitive, but not,
not an intellectual mind, and to have been impelled by circumstances to get out and earn my living and help with the instal-
ments on the house. I believe that had my early formative years
been passed in more assured circumstances I might quite easily
have slipped into preciousness; as it was I merely had to slip *out* of
precociousness and bring home the bacon. The world of the
theatre is a strong forcing-house, and I believe I knew more
about the basic facts of life by the age of fourteen than the more
carefully untutored knew at twenty-five. In any event, my own
peculiar circumstances suited me and on the whole the results
haven't been too bad.

(*Diary, 21 December 1967*)

The Boy Actor

I can remember. I can remember.
The months of November and December
    Were filled for me with peculiar joys
So different from those of other boys

23

For other boys would be counting the days
Until end of term and holiday times
    But I was acting in Christmas plays
While they were taken to pantomimes.
    I didn't envy their Eton suits,
Their children's dances and Christmas trees.
    My life had wonderful substitutes
For such conventional treats as these.
    I didn't envy their country larks,
Their organised games in panelled halls:
    While they made snowmen in stately parks
I was counting the curtain calls.

    I remember the auditions, the nerve-racking auditions:
    Darkened auditorium and empty, dusty stage,
    Little girls in ballet dresses practising 'positions',
    Gentlemen with pince-nez asking you your age.
    Hopefulness and nervousness struggling within you,
    Dreading that familiar phrase, 'Thank you dear, no more.'
    Straining every muscle, every tendon, every sinew
    To do your dance much better than you'd ever done before.
    Think of your performance. Never mind the others,
    Never mind the pianist, talent must prevail.
    Never mind the baleful eyes of other children's mothers
    Glaring from the corners and willing you to fail.

I can remember. I can remember.
The months of November and December
    Were more significant to me
Than other months could ever be
    For they were the months of high romance
When destiny waited on tiptoe,
    When every boy actor stood a chance
Of getting into a Christmas show,
    Not for me the dubious heaven
Of being some prefect's protégé!
    Not for me the Second Eleven.
For me, two performances a day.

FORTUNE

DUCHESS

ADELPHI

Ah those first rehearsals! Only very few lines:
Rushing home to mother, learning them by heart,
'Enter Left through window' – Dots to mark the cue lines:
'Exit with the others' – Still, it *was* a part.
Opening performance; legs a bit unsteady,
Dedicated tension, shivers down my spine,
Powder, grease and eye-black, sticks of make-up ready,
Leichner number three and number five and number nine.
World of strange enchantment, magic for a small boy
Dreaming of the future, reaching for the crown,
Rigid in the dressing-room, listening for the call-boy
'Overture Beginners – Everybody Down!'

I can remember. I can remember.
The months of November and December,
    Although climatically cold and damp,
Meant more to me than Aladdin's lamp.
    I see myself, having got a job,
Walking on wings along the Strand,
    Uncertain whether to laugh or sob
And clutching tightly my mother's hand.
    I never cared who scored the goal
Or which side won the silver cup,
    I never learned to bat or bowl
But I heard the curtain going up.

*Those early years were divided between Christmas shows in London,
such as* Where the Rainbow Ends, *and touring the provinces in reliable successes like* Peter Pan *and* Charley's Aunt. *One engagement took the young actor to Liverpool and Manchester. On the train from Euston he met . . .*

. . . a vivacious child with ringlets to whom I took an instant
fancy. She wore a black satin coat and a black velvet military hat
with a peak, her face was far from pretty, but tremendously alive.
She was very *mondaine*, carried a handbag with a powder-puff
and frequently dabbed her generously turned-up nose. She confided to me that her name was Gertrude Lawrence, but that I was

to call her Gert because everybody did, that she was fourteen, just over licensing age, that she had been in *The Miracle* at Olympia and *Fifinella* at the Gaiety, Manchester. She then gave me an orange and told me a few mildly dirty stories, and I loved her from then onwards.

In the years that followed Gertrude Lawrence danced ahead as an actress and singer while Coward struggled to establish himself not only as a performer but as a writer as well.

I appeared at crowded auditions wearing an immaculate suit and an air of amused condescension which deceived nobody and merely succeeded in irritating the other aspirants. I had written a number of light songs during the past years, and I sang them repeatedly, accompanying myself on the piano. There was a sentimental ballad: 'Tamarisk Town', and a bright 'Point' number: 'Forbidden Fruit', which I think is worthy of record as it was the first complete lyric I ever wrote. The perceptive reader will, I am sure, detect, even in this very youthful effort, that unfortunate taint of worldly cynicism which, I am so frequently told, degrades much of my later work.

Forbidden Fruit

Verse

Ordinary man invariably sighs
Vainly for what cannot be,
If he's in an orchard he will cast his eyes
Up into the highest tree,
There may be a lot of windfalls
Lying all around,
But you'll never see a man enjoy the fruit that's on the ground.

Refrain 1

Every peach out of reach is attractive
'Cos it's just a little bit too high,
And you'll find that every man

Will try to pluck it if he can
As he passes by.
For the brute loves the fruit that's forbidden
And I'll bet you half a crown
He'll appreciate the flavour of it much much more
If he has to climb a bit to shake it down.

Refrain 2

Every peach out of reach is attractive
'Cos it's just a little bit too high,
Though it isn't very sane
To make the things you can't attain,
Still you always try.
If you find that you're blind with devotion
For delightful Mrs Brown,
You'll appreciate eloping with her much much more
If her husband comes along and knocks you down.

Refrain 3

Every peach out of reach is attractive
'Cos it's just a little bit too high,
Even well-brought-up young girls
Will look at other women's pearls
With a yearning eye.
If they fight day and night persevering
And a small string they collect,
They'll appreciate the colour of them much much more
If they've sacrificed a little self-respect.

I can only suppose that this cold-blooded realism was too much for the managers, because they neither made any offers for me nor for the song. I remember on one occasion Beatrice Lillie incurred the grave displeasure of André Charlot by bringing me in to sing for him before an afternoon rehearsal. He informed her afterwards that he would not have his valuable time wasted by trivial young composers who played the piano badly and sang worse, and that never, in any circumstances, was she to do such a thing again.

The Twenties

The new decade brought with it an improvement in Coward's fortunes. Although he continued to act in other people's plays, he began to find success with those he wrote himself. I'll Leave it to You came to London in 1920 and The Young Idea was produced in 1922. At the end of that year Coward found an enthusiastic audience for his words and music.

André Charlot had changed his mind about this 'trivial young composer' so completely that he commissioned him to write songs and sketches for London Calling, a revue with Gertrude Lawrence, Maisie Gay and Coward himself.

And so it was . . . ten years after their first meeting on a train journey to Manchester, Noël and Gertie were together again and she was singing one of his songs. It may have seemed inconsequential then; now it seems to pin down that butterfly period for us.

Parisian Pierrot

Verse 1

Fantasy in olden days
In varying and different ways
Was very much in vogue,
Columbine and Pantaloon,
A wistful Pierrot 'neath the moon,
And Harlequin a rogue.
Nowadays Parisians of leisure
Wake the echo of an old refrain,
Each some ragged effigy will treasure
For his pleasure,
Till the shadows of their story live again.

Verse 2

Mournfulness has always been
The keynote of a Pierrot scene,
When passion plays a part,

Pierrot in a tragic pose
Will kiss a faded silver rose
With sadness in his heart.
Some day soon he'll leave his tears behind him,
Comedy comes laughing down the street,
Columbine will fly to him
Admiring and desiring,
Laying love and adoration at his feet.

Refrain

Parisian Pierrot,
Society's hero,
The Lord of a day,
The Rue de la Paix
Is under your sway,
The world may flatter
But what does that matter,
They'll never shatter
Your gloom profound,
Parisian Pierrot,
Your spirit's at zero,
Divinely forlorn,
With exquisite scorn
From sunset to dawn,
The limbo is calling,
Your star will be falling,
As soon as the clock goes round.

'Divinely forlorn' is a phrase which might be applied to the character which Coward created for himself to play in his first great success. Nicky Lancaster was the character and The Vortex *was the play which established Noël Coward in the theatre of the Twenties. His leading lady was Lilian Braithwaite and the opening was a memorable one.*

The first person to clutch my hand afterwards was Michael Arlen. His face was white with excitement and he said: 'I'd be so proud, so *very* proud if I had written it.' . . .

There it was real and complete, my first big moment. I don't remember exactly how I felt. I do know that I was tired. We were all tired. I know also that I recognised a solidity underlying all the excitement; this time I really had done it. The cheering and applause had been no louder than it had been for *I'll Leave it to You* and *The Young Idea*. If anything it had been a trifle less, owing to the smallness of the Everyman Theatre. The back-stage enthusiasts had used the same phrases; their superlatives were still in my ears; the same superlatives as before; the same 'divines', 'darlings', 'brilliants', and 'marvellouses'. The same fervent embraces and handshakes; the same glistening eyes. But this time there was a subtle difference. Lilian said wearily: 'Do you think we are all right?' And I knew, and she knew that I knew, that the question was merely rhetorical, a routine gesture of diffidence. We were all right, more than all right. We were a smash hit.

In spite of his triumph Coward continued to live with his parents at 111 Ebury Street, where his mother took in lodgers. The decoration of his own apartment was revolutionised with the help of Gladys Calthorp, the theatrical designer.

I ordered new chintz covers for my sitting-room and had my bedroom done over in pillar-box scarlet, a decision which I afterwards regretted. Gladys set her seal on this by painting, out of the goodness of her heart and the deeps of her erotic imagination, a few murals to brighten up the room in case the scarlet paint became too monotonous. There were two pink nudes over the fireplace, and a third doing its languid best to disguise what was quite obviously a po cupboard. It was in the midst of this misguided splendour that I was unwise enough to be photographed in bed wearing a Chinese dressing-gown and an expression of advanced degeneracy. This last was accidental and was caused by blinking at the flashlight, but it emblazoned my unquestionable decadence firmly on to the minds of all who saw it. It even brought forth a letter of indignant protest from a retired Brigadier-General in Gloucestershire.

When he returned to the musical theatre, Coward fully expected to call the tune, but once again he came up against an unsympathetic impresario.

Soon after the opening of *The Vortex* I started work on a revue for Cochran. This had been tentatively discussed before. There had been an interview with C. B. in his office in Old Bond Street in course of which we bickered for about two hours because he wanted me only to write the book of the revue, and I wished to compose the entire score as well. Finally his armour of evasive politeness cracked, and he was forced to say that he was very sorry, but he frankly did not consider my music good enough to carry a whole show, and that he intended to engage Philip Braham as composer. That settled it for the time being, and I retired, vanquished, to concentrate on ideas for sketches and burlesques.

The ideas came swiftly and, oddly enough, nearly every idea carried with it its accompanying song. In my planning of the show almost every scene led up to a number, and so when the revue was complete it was discovered, to the embarrassment of everyone but me, that with the exception of three numbers by Philip Braham for which I had written the lyrics, a few odd pieces of classical music for use in ballets, etc., and one interpolated song for Delysia, the whole score, book and lyrics were mine.

On With the Dance, *with Alice Delysia as the star, went into production while Coward was still playing the lead in* The Vortex. *For the final rehearsals in Manchester he took two nights off, leaving his understudy, John Gielgud, to appear in his place.*

Those three days were on the whole unpleasant, although fraught with incident. In the first place I discovered soon after my arrival that my name was not on the bills at all. The show was labelled 'Charles B. Cochran's Revue', which, considering that I had done three-quarters of the score, all the lyrics, all of the book, and directed all the dialogue scenes, and several of the numbers, seemed to be a slight overstatement. I went roaring back from the theatre to the Midland Hotel and attacked Cockie in his bathroom. I'm not at all sure that I didn't deprive him of

31

his towel while I shrieked at him over the noise of the water gurg-
ling down the plug-hole. I will say, however, that he retained his
dignity magnificently, far more than I, and in due course calmed
me down and gave me some sherry. It is odd that in all the years
I have since worked with Cockie, that show was the only one
over which we have ever quarrelled. I think the psychological
explanation must be that then, in those early days of our associ-
ation, we had neither of us estimated accurately enough our
respective egos. And a couple of tougher ones it would be difficult to find.

Cockie and I had still one more battle, this time over 'Poor Little Rich Girl', which he considered too dreary and wished to take
out of the show. I fought like a steer, backed up by Delysia, and
fortunately for all concerned we won, as it turned out to be the
big song hit of the revue.

Poor Little Rich Girl

Verse

You're only
A baby,
You're lonely,
And maybe
Some day soon you'll know
The tears
You are tasting
Are years
You are wasting,
Life's a bitter foe,
With fate it's no use competing,
Youth is so terribly fleeting;
By dancing
Much faster,
You're chancing
Disaster,
Time alone will show.

Refrain

Poor little rich girl,
You're a bewitched girl,
Better beware!
Laughing at danger,
Virtue a stranger,
Better take care!
The life you lead sets all your nerves a-jangle,
Your love affairs are in a hopeless tangle,
Though you're a child, dear,
Your life's a wild typhoon,
In lives of leisure
The craze for pleasure
Steadily grows.
Cocktails and laughter,
But what comes after?
Nobody knows.
You're weaving love into a mad jazz pattern,
Ruled by Pantaloon.
Poor little rich girl, don't drop a stitch too soon.

As soon as Coward returned to London and the cast of The Vortex, *another of his plays,* Fallen Angels, *went into rehearsal with Edna Best and Tallulah Bankhead. When it opened it attracted reviews very different from those the author had received before.*

The Press notices for *Fallen Angels* were vituperative to the point of incoherence. No epithet was spared. It was described as vulgar, disgusting, shocking, nauseating, vile, obscene, degenerate, etc., etc. The idea of two gently nurtured young women playing a drinking scene together was apparently too degrading a spectacle for even the most hardened and worldly critics. The *Daily Express* even went so far as to allude to these two wayward creatures as 'suburban sluts'.

All this was capital for the box-office and the play ran for several months.

From The Vortex *onwards and for the next quarter of a century, the sets for all Coward's plays were designed by Gladys Calthrop, one of his closest friends and most trusted colleagues. When he returned from the American tour of* The Vortex *she was present at the birth of something quite different from the plays and revues which Coward had written before.*

The idea of *Bitter Sweet* was born in the early summer of that year, 1928. It appeared quite unexpectedly and with no other motivation beyond the fact that I had vaguely discussed with Gladys the possibilities of writing a romantic Operette. She and I were staying with Ronald Peake, her family solicitor, in Surrey, and an hour or so before we were due to leave, Mr Peake happened to play to us on the gramophone a new German orchestral record of *Die Fledermaus*. Immediately a confused picture of uniforms, bustles, chandeliers and gas-lit cafés formed in my mind, and later, when we were driving over Wimbledon Common, we drew the car to a standstill by the roadside, and in the shade of a giant horse-chestnut tree mapped out roughly the story of Sarah Linden.

The uniforms, bustles, chandeliers and gas-lit cafés all fell into place eagerly, as though they had been waiting in the limbo for just this cue to enter.

The show contains one of the best-known melodies of the twentieth century, a tune that has been played by every musical combination from the symphony orchestra to the lonely cocktail piano; but it did not present itself until the eleventh hour. Coward was in New York again, appearing in his revue This Year of Grace.

During that winter, January and February, 1929, I finished *Bitter Sweet*, on which I had been working intermittently for the last few months. The book had been completed long since, but the score had been causing me trouble, until one day, when I was in a taxi on my way back to the apartment after a matinée, the 'I'll See You Again' waltz dropped into my mind, whole and complete, during a twenty minutes' traffic block.

I'll See You Again

CARL: Now Miss Sarah, if you please,
Sing a scale for me . . .
Take a breath and then reprise
In a different key.
All my life I shall remember knowing you,
All the pleasure I have found in showing you
The different ways
That one may phrase
The changing light, and changing shade;
Happiness that must die,
Melodies that must fly,
Memories that must fade,
Dusty and forgotten by and by.

SARAH: Learning scales will never seem so sweet again
Till our Destiny shall let us meet again.

CARL: The will of Fate
May come too late.

SARAH: When I'm recalling these hours we've had
Why will the foolish tears
Tremble across the years,
Why shall I feel so sad,
Treasuring the memory of these days
Always?

CARL: I'll see you again,
Whenever Spring breaks through again;
Time may lie heavy between,
But what has been
Is past forgetting.

SARAH: This sweet memory,
Across the years will come to me;

Though my world may go awry,
In my heart will ever lie
Just the echo of a sigh,
Goodbye.

My first choice for Sarah had been Gertie Lawrence, but when the score was almost done, she and I both realised that her voice, although light and charming, was not strong enough to carry such a heavy singing role. She was naturally disappointed and I promised that the next play I wrote would be especially for her.

There is one other song in Bitter Sweet *which became an indispensable part of the Noël Coward legend. He sang it all over the world, on stage, on radio and television and always in cabaret. It became not merely a signature tune but also a creed and an epitome of his great gift, 'a talent to amuse'. In the original operetta it is sung by Manon, a nightclub entertainer.*

If Love Were All

Life is a very rough and tumble,
For a humble
Diseuse,
One can betray one's troubles never,
Whatever
Occurs,
Night after night,
Have to look bright,
Whether you're well or ill
People must laugh their fill.
You mustn't sleep
Till dawn comes creeping.
Though I never really grumble
Life's a jumble.
Indeed—
And in my efforts to succeed
I've had to formulate a creed—

Refrain

I believe in doing what I can,
In crying when I must,
In laughing when I choose.
Heigho, if love were all
I should be lonely,
I believe the more you love a man,
The more you give your trust,
The more you're bound to lose.
Although when shadows fall
I think if only—
Somebody splendid really needed me,
Someone affectionate and dear,
Cares would be ended if I knew that he
Wanted to have me near.
But I believe that since my life began
The most I've had is just
A talent to amuse.
Heigho, if love were all!

Though life buffets me obscenely,
It serenely
Goes on.
Although I question its conclusion,
Illusion
Is gone.
Frequently I
Put a bit by
Safe for a rainy day.
Nobody here can say
To what, indeed,
The years are leading.
Fate may often treat me meanly,
But I keenly
Pursue
A little mirage in the blue.
Determination helps me through.

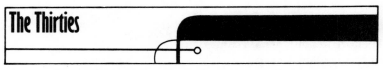

The Thirties

In 1929 Coward had directed both the British and American produc-
tions of Bitter Sweet. *By the time the show opened in New York he*
was a hugely successful but tired man, and he planned an extended
holiday in the Far East.

It occurred to me that I had been living in a crowd for too long;
not only a crowd of friends, enemies and acquaintances, but a
crowd of events: events that had followed each other so swiftly
that the value of them, their causes and effects, their significance, had escaped me. My nervous energy, always excessive, had
carried me so far. My determination, ambition and almost
hysterical industry had been rewarded generously, perhaps too
generously. At all events I could congratulate myself whole-
heartedly on one count: I had realised, I hoped not too late, the
necessity for space, and had deliberately broken away.

My lyric writing during 'The Thirties' started very satisfactorily
with 'Mad Dogs and Englishmen'. The idea of it and the rhythm
of it got into my head when I was driving, in February 1930, from
Hanoi in Tonkin to Saigon. This drive took about a week and
while jungles and rivers and mountains and rice fields were
unrolling by the window of the car, I wrestled in my mind with
the complicated rhythms and rhymes of the song until finally it
was complete, without even the aid of pencil or paper. I sang it
triumphantly and unaccompanied to my travelling companion,
Jeffery Amherst, on the verandah of a small jungle guest house.
Not only Jeffery but the gekko lizards and the tree frogs gave
every vocal indication of enthusiasm.

(*The Lyrics of Noël Coward,* 1965)

Mad Dogs and Englishmen

In tropical climes there are certain times of day
When all the citizens retire
To tear their clothes off and perspire.
It's one of those rules that the greatest fools obey,
Because the sun is much too sultry
And one must avoid its ultry-violet ray.

Papalaka papalaka papalaka boo,
Papalaka papalaka papalaka boo,
Digariga digariga digariga doo,
Digariga digariga digariga doo.

The natives grieve when the white men leave their huts,
Because they're obviously definitely nuts!

Mad dogs and Englishmen
Go out in the midday sun.
The Japanese don't care to,
The Chinese wouldn't dare to,
Hindoos and Argentines sleep firmly from twelve to one.
But Englishmen detest a siesta.
In the Philippines
There are lovely screens
To protect you from the glare.
In the Malay States
There are hats like plates
Which the Britishers won't wear.
At twelve noon
The natives swoon
And no further work is done.
But mad dogs and Englishmen
Go out in the midday sun.

It's such a surprise for the Eastern eyes to see
That though the English are effete,

They're quite impervious to heat.
When the white man rides every native hides in glee,
Because the simple creatures hope he
Will impale his solar topee on a tree.

> Bolyboly bolyboly bolyboly baa,
> Bolyboly bolyboly bolyboly baa,
> Habaninny habaninny habaninny haa,
> Habaninny habaninny habaninny haa.

It seems such a shame
When the English claim
The earth
That they give rise to such hilarity and mirth.

Mad dogs and Englishmen
Go out in the midday sun.
The toughest Burmese bandit
Can never understand it.
In Rangoon the heat of noon
Is just what the natives shun.
They put their Scotch or Rye down
And lie down
In a jungle town
Where the sun beats down.
To the rage of man and beast
The English garb
Of the English sahib
Merely gets a bit more creased.
In Bangkok
At twelve o'clock
They foam at the mouth and run,
But mad dogs and Englishmen
Go out in the midday sun.

Mad dogs and Englishmen
Go out in the midday sun.
The smallest Malay rabbit

Deplores this stupid habit.
In Hong Kong
They strike a gong
And fire off a noonday gun
To reprimand each inmate
Who's in late.
In the mangrove swamps
Where the python romps
There is peace from twelve till two.
Even caribous
Lie around and snooze,
For there's nothing else to do.
In Bengal
To move at all
Is seldom, if ever done,
But mad dogs and Englishmen
Go out in the midday sun.

Gertie Lawrence, the night before I had left New York, had given a farewell party for me and, as a going-away present, a little gold book from Cartier's which when opened and placed on the writing-table in my cabin disclosed a clock, calendar and thermometer on one side, and an extremely pensive photograph of Gertie herself on the other. This rich gift, although I am sure prompted by the least ulterior of motives, certainly served as a delicate reminder that I had promised to write a play for us both, and I gazed daily, often with irritation, at that anxious *retroussé* face while my mind voyaged barrenly through eighteenth-century salons, Second Empire drawing-rooms and modern cocktail bars in search of some inspiring echo, some slight thread of plot that might suitably unite us in either comedy, tragedy or sentiment . . .

The Imperial Hotel in Tokyo was grand and comfortable, and was renowned for having stood firm during the big earthquake. A wire was handed me from Jeffery saying that he had missed a boat in Shanghai and wouldn't be with me for three days . . .

The night before he arrived I went to bed early as I wanted to greet him as brightly as possible at seven in the morning, but the moment I switched out the lights, Gertie appeared in a white Molyneux dress on a terrace in the South of France and refused to go again until four a.m., by which time *Private Lives*, title and all, had constructed itself.

A bout of influenza laid me low in Shanghai, and I lay, sweating gloomily, in my bedroom in the Cathay Hotel for several days. The ensuing convalescence, however, was productive, for I utilised it by writing *Private Lives*. The idea by now seemed ripe enough to have a shot at, so I started it, propped up in bed with a writing-block and an Eversharp pencil, and completed it, roughly, in four days.

So, in September 1930, Noël and Gertie embarked on a short provincial tour of the play that set the seal on their partnership.

Adrianne Allen (Mrs Raymond Massey) played 'Sibyl' in *Private Lives*, and Laurence Olivier, 'Victor'. The whole tour was swathed in luxury. Adrianne travelled in a car, so did Gertie and so did I, the touring days of the past belonged to another world. Assurance of success seemed to be emblazoned on the play from the first, we had few qualms, played to capacity business and enjoyed ourselves thoroughly. We felt, I think rightly, that there was a shine on us.

In London we opened in a new theatre, the Phoenix. We were an immediate hit, and our three months' limited engagement was sold out during the first week. It was an interesting play to play, naturally more interesting for Gertie and me than it was for Larry and Adrianne. We had the parts, or rather, the part, as 'Elyot' and 'Amanda' are practically synonymous. The play's fabric was light and required light handling. Gertie was brilliant. Everything she had been in my mind when I originally conceived the idea in Tokyo came to life on the stage: the witty, quicksilver delivery of lines; the romantic quality, tender and alluring; the swift, brittle rages; even the white Molyneux dress.

PRIVATE LIVES

Dramatis Personae

AMANDA PRYNNE
VICTOR PRYNNE, her husband
LOUISE, a maid
SIBYL CHASE
ELYOT CHASE, her husband

ACT I
The Terrace of a Hotel in France. Summer evening.

ACT II
Amanda's flat in Paris. A few days later. Evening.

ACT III
The same. The next morning.

TIME: *The Present.*

44

Act I

The Scene is the terrace of a hotel in France. There are two french windows at the back opening on to two separate suites. The terrace space is divided by a line of small trees in tubs, and, down stage, running parallel with the footlights, there is a low stone balustrade. Upon each side of the line of tree tubs is a set of suitable terrace furniture, a swinging seat, two or three chairs, and a table. There are orange and white awnings shading the windows, as it is summer.

When the curtain rises it is about eight o'clock in the evening. There is an orchestra playing not very far off. SIBYL CHASE *opens the windows on the Right, and steps out on to the terrace. She is very pretty and blonde, and smartly dressed in travelling clothes. She comes down stage, stretches her arms wide with a little sigh of satisfaction, and regards the view with an ecstatic expression.*

SIBYL [*calling*]: Elli, Elli, dear, do come out. It's so lovely.

ELYOT [*inside*]: Just a minute.

> [*After a pause* ELYOT *comes out. He is about thirty, quite slim and pleasant looking, and also in travelling clothes. He walks right down to the balustrade and looks thoughtfully at the view.* SIBYL *stands beside him, and slips her arm through his.*]

ELYOT: Not so bad.

SIBYL: It's heavenly. Look at the lights of that yacht reflected in the water. Oh dear, I'm so happy.

ELYOT [*smiling*]: Are you?

SIBYL: Aren't you?

ELYOT: Of course I am. Tremendously happy.

SIBYL: Just to think, here we are, you and I, married!

ELYOT: Yes, things have come to a pretty pass.

SIBYL: Don't laugh at me, you mustn't be *blasé* about honeymoons just because this is your second.

ELYOT [*frowning*]: That's silly.

SIBYL: Have I annoyed you by saying that?

ELYOT: Just a little.

SIBYL: O darling, I'm so sorry. [*She holds her face up to his.*] Kiss me.

ELYOT [*doing so*]: There.

SIBYL: Ummm, not so very enthusiastic.

ELYOT [*kissing her again*]: That better?

SIBYL: Three times, please, I'm superstitious.

ELYOT [*kissing her*]: You really are very sweet.

SIBYL: Are you glad you married me?

ELYOT: Of course I am.

SIBYL: How glad?

ELYOT: Incredibly, magnificently glad.

SIBYL: How lovely.

ELYOT: We ought to go in and dress.

SIBYL: Gladder than before?

ELYOT: Why do you keep harping on that?

SIBYL: It's in my mind, and yours too, I expect.

ELYOT: It isn't anything of the sort.

SIBYL: She was pretty, wasn't she? Amanda?

ELYOT: Very pretty.

SIBYL: Prettier than I am?

ELYOT: Much.

SIBYL: Elyot!

ELYOT: She was pretty and sleek, and her hands were long and slim, and her legs were long and slim, and she danced like an angel. You dance very poorly, by the way.

SIBYL: Could she play the piano as well as I can?

ELYOT: She couldn't play the piano at all.

SIBYL [*triumphantly*]: Aha! Had she my talent for organisation?

ELYOT: No, but she hadn't your mother either.

SIBYL: I don't believe you like mother.

ELYOT: Like her! I can't bear her.

SIBYL: Elyot! She's a darling, underneath.

ELYOT: I never got underneath.

SIBYL: It makes me unhappy to think you don't like mother.

ELYOT: Nonsense. I believe the only reason you married me was to get away from her.

SIBYL: I married you because I loved you.

ELYOT: Oh dear, oh dear, oh dear, oh dear!

SIBYL: I love you far more than Amanda loved you. I'd never make you miserable like she did.

46

ELYOT: We made each other miserable.

SIBYL: It was all her fault, you know it was.

ELYOT [*with vehemence*]: Yes, it was. Entirely her fault.

SIBYL: She was a fool to lose you.

ELYOT: We lost each other.

SIBYL: She lost you, with her violent tempers and carryings on.

ELYOT: Will you stop talking about Amanda?

SIBYL: But I'm very glad, because if she hadn't been uncontrolled, and wicked, and unfaithful, we shouldn't be here
now.

ELYOT: She wasn't unfaithful.

SIBYL: How do you know? I bet she was. I bet she was unfaithful
every five minutes.

ELYOT: It would take a far more concentrated woman than
Amanda to be unfaithful every five minutes.

SIBYL [*anxiously*]: You do hate her, don't you?

ELYOT: No, I don't hate her. I think I despise her.

SIBYL [*with satisfaction*]: That's much worse.

ELYOT: And yet I'm sorry for her.

SIBYL: Why?

ELYOT: Because she's marked for tragedy; she's bound to make
a mess of everything.

SIBYL: If it's all her fault, I don't see that it matters much.

ELYOT: She has some very good qualities.

SIBYL: Considering what a hell she made of your life, I think
you are very nice about her. Most men would be vindictive.

ELYOT: What's the use of that? It's all over now, such a long
time ago.

SIBYL: Five years isn't very long.

ELYOT [*seriously*]: Yes it is.

SIBYL: Do you think you could ever love her again?

ELYOT: Now then, Sibyl.

SIBYL: But could you?

ELYOT: Of course not, I love you.

SIBYL: Yes, but you love me differently; I know that.

ELYOT: More wisely perhaps.

SIBYL: I'm glad. I'd rather have that sort of love.

ELYOT: You're right. Love is no use unless it's wise, and kind,

47

and undramatic. Something steady and sweet, to smooth out your nerves when you're tired. Something tremendously cosy; and unflurried by scenes and jealousies. That's what I want, what I've always wanted really. O my dear, I do hope it's not going to be dull for you.

SIBYL: Sweetheart, as tho' you could ever be dull.

ELYOT: I'm much older than you.

SIBYL: Not so very much.

ELYOT: Seven years.

SIBYL [snuggling up to him]: The music has stopped now and you can hear the sea.

ELYOT: We'll bathe tomorrow morning.

SIBYL: I mustn't get sunburnt.

ELYOT: Why not?

SIBYL: I hate it on women.

ELYOT: Very well, you shan't then. I hope you don't hate it on men.

SIBYL: Of course I don't. It's suitable to men.

ELYOT: You're a completely feminine little creature, aren't you?

SIBYL: Why do you say that?

ELYOT: Everything in its place.

SIBYL: What do you mean?

ELYOT: If you feel you'd like me to smoke a pipe, I'll try and master it.

SIBYL: I like a man to be a man, if that's what you mean.

ELYOT: Are you going to understand me, and manage me?

SIBYL: I'm going to try to understand you.

ELYOT: Run me without my knowing it?

SIBYL [withdrawing slightly]: I think you're being a little unkind.

ELYOT: No, I don't mean to be. I was only wondering.

SIBYL: Well?

ELYOT: I was wondering what was going on inside your mind, what your plans are really?

SIBYL: Plans? O Elli!

ELYOT: Apart from loving me and all that, you must have plans.

SIBYL: I haven't the faintest idea what you're talking about.

ELYOT: Perhaps it's subconscious then, age-old instincts working away deep down, mincing up little bits of experience for future use, watching me carefully like a little sharp-eyed, blonde kitten.

SIBYL: How can you be so horrid.

ELYOT: I said Kitten, not Cat.

SIBYL: Kittens grow into cats.

ELYOT: Let that be a warning to you.

SIBYL [*slipping her arm through his again*]: What's the matter, darling; are you hungry?

ELYOT: Not a bit.

SIBYL: You're very strange all of a sudden, and rather cruel. Just because I'm feminine, it doesn't mean that I'm crafty and calculating.

ELYOT: I didn't say you were either of those things.

SIBYL: I hate these half masculine women who go banging about.

ELYOT: I hate anybody who goes banging about.

SIBYL: I should think you needed a little quiet womanliness after Amanda.

ELYOT: Why will you keep on talking about her?

SIBYL: It's natural enough, isn't it?

ELYOT: What do you want to find out?

SIBYL: Why did you really let her divorce you?

ELYOT: She divorced me for cruelty, and flagrant infidelity. I spent a whole weekend at Brighton with a lady called Vera Williams. She had the nastiest looking hair brush I have ever seen.

SIBYL: Misplaced chivalry, I call it. Why didn't you divorce her?

ELYOT: It would not have been the action of a gentleman, whatever that may mean.

SIBYL: I think she got off very lightly.

ELYOT: Once and for all, will you stop talking about her.

SIBYL: Yes, Elli dear.

ELYOT: I don't wish to see her again or hear her name mentioned.

SIBYL: Very well, darling.

ELYOT: Is that understood?

SIBYL: Yes, darling. Where did you spend your honeymoon?

ELYOT: St Moritz. Be quiet.

SIBYL: I hate St Moritz.

ELYOT: So do I, bitterly.

SIBYL: Was she good on skis?

ELYOT: Do you want to dine downstairs here, or at the Casino?

SIBYL: I love you, I love you, I love you.

ELYOT: Good, let's go in and dress.

SIBYL: Kiss me first.

ELYOT [*kissing her*]: Casino?

SIBYL: Yes. Are you a gambler? You never told me.

ELYOT: Every now and then.

SIBYL: I shall come and sit just behind your chair and bring you luck.

ELYOT: That will be fatal.

[*They go off into their suite. There is a slight pause and then* VICTOR PRYNNE *enters from the Left suite. He is quite nice looking, about thirty or thirty-five. He is dressed in a light travelling suit. He sniffs the air, looks at the view, and then turns back to the window.*]

VICTOR [*calling*]: Mandy.

AMANDA [*inside*]: What?

VICTOR: Come outside, the view is wonderful.

AMANDA: I'm still damp from the bath. Wait a minute—

[VICTOR *lights a cigarette. Presently* AMANDA *comes out on to the terrace. She is quite exquisite with a gay face and a perfect figure. At the moment she is wearing a négligé.*]

I shall catch pneumonia, that's what I shall catch.

VICTOR [*looking at her*]: God!

AMANDA: I beg your pardon?

VICTOR: You look wonderful.

AMANDA: Thank you, darling.

VICTOR: Like a beautiful advertisement for something.

AMANDA: Nothing peculiar, I hope.

VICTOR: I can hardly believe it's true. You and I, here alone together, married!

AMANDA [*rubbing her face on his shoulder*]: That stuff's very rough.

VICTOR: Don't you like it?

AMANDA: A bit hearty, isn't it?

50

VICTOR: Do you love me?

AMANDA: Of course, that's why I'm here.

VICTOR: More than—

AMANDA: Now then, none of that.

VICTOR: No, but do you love me more than you loved Elyot?

AMANDA: I don't remember, it's such a long time ago.

VICTOR: Not so very long.

AMANDA [*flinging out her arms*]: All my life ago.

VICTOR: I'd like to break his damned neck.

AMANDA [*laughing*]: Why?

VICTOR: For making you unhappy.

AMANDA: It was mutual.

VICTOR: Rubbish! It was all his fault, you know it was.

AMANDA: Yes, it was, now I come to think about it.

VICTOR: Swine!

AMANDA: Don't be so vehement, darling.

VICTOR: I'll never treat you like that.

AMANDA: That's right.

VICTOR: I love you too much.

AMANDA: So did he.

VICTOR: Fine sort of love that is. He struck you once, didn't he?

AMANDA: More than once.

VICTOR: Where?

AMANDA: Several places.

VICTOR: What a cad.

AMANDA: I struck him too. Once I broke four gramophone records over his head. It was very satisfying.

VICTOR: You must have been driven to distraction.

AMANDA: Yes, I was, but don't let's talk about it, please. After all, it's a dreary subject for our honeymoon night.

VICTOR: He didn't know when he was well off.

AMANDA: Look at the lights of that yacht reflected in the water. I wonder whose it is.

VICTOR: We must bathe tomorrow.

AMANDA: Yes. I want to get a nice sunburn.

VICTOR [*reproachfully*]: Mandy!

AMANDA: Why, what's the matter?

VICTOR: I hate sunburnt women.

AMANDA: Why?

VICTOR: It's somehow, well, unsuitable.

AMANDA: It's awfully suitable to me, darling.

VICTOR: Of course if you really want to.

AMANDA: I'm absolutely determined. I've got masses of lovely oil to rub all over myself.

VICTOR: Your skin is so beautiful as it is.

AMANDA: Wait and see. When I'm done a nice crisp brown, you'll fall in love with me all over again.

VICTOR: I couldn't love you more than I do now.

AMANDA: Oh dear. I did so hope our honeymoon was going to be progressive.

VICTOR: Where did you spend the last one?

AMANDA [*warningly*]: Victor.

VICTOR: I want to know.

AMANDA: St Moritz. It was very attractive.

VICTOR: I hate St Moritz.

AMANDA: So do I.

VICTOR: Did he start quarrelling with you right away?

AMANDA: Within the first few days. I put it down to the high altitudes.

VICTOR: And you loved him?

AMANDA: Yes, Victor.

VICTOR: You poor child.

AMANDA: You must try not to be pompous, dear. [*She turns away.*]

VICTOR [*hurt*]: Mandy!

AMANDA: I don't believe I'm a bit like what you think I am.

VICTOR: How do you mean?

AMANDA: I was never a poor child.

VICTOR: Figure of speech, dear, that's all.

AMANDA: I suffered a good deal, and had my heart broken. But it wasn't an innocent girlish heart. It was jagged with sophistication. I've always been sophisticated, far too knowing. That caused many of my rows with Elyot. I irritated him because he knew I could see through him.

VICTOR: I don't mind how much you see through me.

AMANDA: Sweet. [*She kisses him.*]

VICTOR: I'm going to make you happy.

AMANDA: Are you?

VICTOR: Just by looking after you, and seeing that you're all right, you know.

AMANDA [*a trifle wistfully*]: No, I don't know.

VICTOR: I think you love me quite differently from the way you loved Elyot.

AMANDA: Do stop harping on Elyot.

VICTOR: It's true, though, isn't it?

AMANDA: I love you much more calmly, if that's what you mean.

VICTOR: More lastingly?

AMANDA: I expect so.

VICTOR: Do you remember when I first met you?

AMANDA: Yes. Distinctly.

VICTOR: At Marion Vale's party.

AMANDA: Yes.

VICTOR: Wasn't it wonderful?

AMANDA: Not really, dear. It was only redeemed from the completely commonplace by the fact of my having hic-coughs.

VICTOR: I never noticed them.

AMANDA: Love at first sight.

VICTOR: Where did you first meet Elyot?

AMANDA: To hell with Elyot.

VICTOR: Mandy!

AMANDA: I forbid you to mention his name again. I'm sick of the sound of it. You must be raving mad. Here we are on the first night of our honeymoon, with the moon coming up, and the music playing, and all you can do is to talk about my first husband. It's downright sacrilegious.

VICTOR: Don't be angry.

AMANDA: Well, it's very annoying.

VICTOR: Will you forgive me?

AMANDA: Yes; only don't do it again.

VICTOR: I promise.

AMANDA: You'd better go and dress now, you haven't bathed yet.

VICTOR: Where shall we dine, downstairs here, or at the Casino?

AMANDA: The Casino is more fun, I think.

VICTOR: We can play Boule afterwards.

AMANDA: No, we can't, dear.

VICTOR: Don't you like dear old Boule?

AMANDA: No, I hate dear old Boule. We'll play a nice game of Chemin de fer.

VICTOR [*apprehensively*]: Not at the big table?

AMANDA: Maybe at the biggest table.

VICTOR: You're not a terrible gambler, are you?

AMANDA: Inveterate. Chance rules my life.

VICTOR: What nonsense.

AMANDA: How can you say it's nonsense? It was chance meeting you. It was chance falling in love; it's chance that we're here, particularly after your driving. Everything that happens is chance.

VICTOR: You know I feel rather scared of you at close quarters.

AMANDA: That promises to be very embarrassing.

VICTOR: You're somehow different now, wilder than I thought you were, more strained.

AMANDA: Wilder! O Victor, I've never felt less wild in my life. A little strained, I grant you, but that's the newly married atmosphere; you can't expect anything else. Honeymooning is a very overrated amusement.

VICTOR: You say that because you had a ghastly experience before.

AMANDA: There you go again.

VICTOR: It couldn't fail to embitter you a little.

AMANDA: The honeymoon wasn't such a ghastly experience really; it was afterwards that was so awful.

VICTOR: I intend to make you forget it all entirely.

AMANDA: You won't succeed by making constant references to it.

VICTOR: I wish I knew you better.

AMANDA: It's just as well you don't. The 'woman' – in italics – should always retain a certain amount of alluring feminine mystery for the 'man' – also in italics.

54

VICTOR: What about the man? Isn't he allowed to have any mystery?

AMANDA: Absolutely none. Transparent as glass.

VICTOR: Oh, I see.

AMANDA: Never mind, darling; it doesn't necessarily work out like that; it's only supposed to.

VICTOR: I'm glad I'm normal.

AMANDA: What an odd thing to be glad about. Why?

VICTOR: Well, aren't you?

AMANDA: I'm not so sure I'm normal.

VICTOR: O Mandy, of course you are, sweetly, divinely normal.

AMANDA: I haven't any peculiar cravings for Chinamen or old boots, if that's what you mean.

VICTOR [*scandalised*]: Mandy!

AMANDA: I think very few people are completely normal really, deep down in their private lives. It all depends on a combination of circumstances. If all the various cosmic thingummys fuse at the same moment, and the right spark is struck, there's no knowing what one mightn't do. That was the trouble with Elyot and me, we were like two violent acids bubbling about in a nasty little matrimonial bottle.

VICTOR: I don't believe you're nearly as complex as you think you are.

AMANDA: I don't think I'm particularly complex, but I know I'm unreliable.

VICTOR: You're frightening me horribly. In what way unreliable?

AMANDA: I'm so apt to see things the wrong way round.

VICTOR: What sort of things?

AMANDA: Morals. What one should do and what one shouldn't.

VICTOR [*fondly*]: Darling, you're so sweet.

AMANDA: Thank you, Victor, that's most encouraging. You really must have your bath now. Come along.

VICTOR: Kiss me.

AMANDA [*doing so*]: There, dear, hurry now; I've only got to slip my dress on and then I shall be ready.

VICTOR: Give me ten minutes.

AMANDA: I'll bring the cocktails out here when they come.

VICTOR: All right.

AMANDA: Go along now, hurry.

[*They both disappear into their suite. After a moment's pause* ELYOT *steps carefully on to the terrace carrying a tray upon which are two champagne cocktails. He puts the tray down on the table.*]

ELYOT [*calling*]: Sibyl.

SIBYL [*inside*]: Yes.

ELYOT: I've brought the cocktails out here, hurry up.

SIBYL: I can't find my lipstick.

ELYOT: Never mind, send down to the kitchen for some cochineal.

SIBYL: Don't be so silly.

ELYOT: Hurry.

[ELYOT *saunters down to the balustrade. He looks casually over on to the next terrace, and then out at the view. He looks up at the moon and sighs, then he sits down in a chair with his back towards the line of tubs, and lights a cigarette.* AMANDA *steps gingerly on to her terrace carrying a tray with two champagne cocktails on it. She is wearing a charmingly simple evening gown, her cloak is flung over her right shoulder. She places the tray carefully on the table, puts her cloak over the back of a chair, and sits down with her back towards* ELYOT. *She takes a small mirror from her handbag, and scrutinises her face in it. The orchestra downstairs strikes up a new melody. Both* ELYOT *and* AMANDA *give a little start. After a moment,* ELYOT *pensively begins to hum the tune the band is playing. It is a sentimental, romantic little tune.* AMANDA *hears him, and clutches at her throat suddenly as though she were suffocating. Then she jumps up noiselessly, and peers over the line of tubs.* ELYOT, *with his back to her, continues to sing obliviously. She sits down again, relaxing with a gesture almost of despair. Then she looks anxiously over her shoulder at the window in case* VICTOR *should be listening, and then, with a little smile, she takes up the melody herself, clearly.* ELYOT *stops dead and gives a gasp, then he jumps up, and stands looking at her. She continues to sing, pretending not to know that he is there. At the end of the song, she turns slowly, and faces him.*]

AMANDA: Thoughtful of them to play that, wasn't it?

ELYOT [*in a stifled voice*]: What are you doing here?

AMANDA: I'm on honeymoon.

ELYOT: How interesting, so am I.

AMANDA: I hope you're enjoying it.

ELYOT: It hasn't started yet.

AMANDA: Neither has mine.

ELYOT: O my God!

AMANDA: I can't help feeling that this is a little unfortunate.

ELYOT: Are you happy?

AMANDA: Perfectly.

ELYOT: Good. That's all right, then, isn't it?

AMANDA: Are you?

ELYOT: Ecstatically.

AMANDA: I'm delighted to hear it. We shall probably meet again sometime. Au revoir! [*She turns.*]

ELYOT [*firmly*]: Goodbye.

[*She goes indoors without looking back. He stands gazing after her with an expression of horror on his face.* SIBYL *comes brightly on to the terrace in a very pretty evening frock.*]

SIBYL: Cocktail, please. [ELYOT *doesn't answer.*] Elli, what's the matter?

ELYOT: I feel very odd.

SIBYL: Odd, what do you mean? Ill?

ELYOT: Yes, ill.

SIBYL [*alarmed*]: What sort of ill?

ELYOT: We must leave at once.

SIBYL: Leave!

ELYOT: Yes, dear. Leave immediately.

SIBYL: Elli!

ELYOT: I have a strange foreboding.

SIBYL: You must be mad.

ELYOT: Listen, darling. I want you to be very sweet, and patient, and understanding, and not be upset, or ask any questions, or anything. I have an absolute conviction that our whole future happiness depends upon our leaving here instantly.

SIBYL: Why?

ELYOT: I can't tell you why.

SIBYL: But we've only just come.

ELYOT: I know that, but it can't be helped.

SIBYL: What's happened, what has happened?

ELYOT: Nothing has happened.

SIBYL: You've gone out of your mind.

ELYOT: I haven't gone out of my mind, but I shall if we stay here another hour.

SIBYL: You're not drunk, are you?

ELYOT: Of course I'm not drunk. What time have I had to get drunk?

SIBYL: Come down and have some dinner, darling, and then you'll feel ever so much better.

ELYOT: It's no use trying to humour me. I'm serious.

SIBYL: But darling, please be reasonable. We've only just arrived; everything's unpacked. It's our first night together. We can't go away now.

ELYOT: We can have our first night together in Paris.

SIBYL: We shouldn't get there until the small hours.

ELYOT [*with a great effort at calmness*]: Now please, Sibyl, I know it sounds crazy to you, and utterly lacking in reason and sense, but I've got second sight over certain things. I'm almost psychic. I've got the most extraordinary sensation of impending disaster. If we stay here something appalling will happen. I know it.

SIBYL [*firmly*]: Hysterical nonsense.

ELYOT: It isn't hysterical nonsense. Presentiments are far from being nonsense. Look at the woman who cancelled her passage on the *Titanic*. All because of a presentiment.

SIBYL: I don't see what that has to do with it.

ELYOT: It has everything to do with it. She obeyed her instincts, that's what she did, and saved her life. All I ask is to be allowed to obey my instincts.

SIBYL: Do you mean that there's going to be an earthquake or something?

ELYOT: Very possibly, very possibly indeed, or perhaps a violent explosion.

SIBYL: They don't have earthquakes in France.

ELYOT: On the contrary, only the other day they felt a distinct shock at Toulon.

SIBYL: Yes, but that's in the south where it's hot.

ELYOT: Don't quibble, Sibyl.

SIBYL: And as for explosions, there's nothing here that can explode.

ELYOT: Oho, isn't there.

SIBYL: Yes, but Elli—

ELYOT: Darling, be sweet. Bear with me. I beseech you to bear with me.

SIBYL: I don't understand. It's horrid of you to do this.

ELYOT: I'm not doing anything. I'm only asking you, imploring you to come away from this place.

SIBYL: But I love it here.

ELYOT: There are thousands of other places far nicer.

SIBYL: It's a pity we didn't go to one of them.

ELYOT: Now, listen, Sibyl—

SIBYL: Yes, but why are you behaving like this, why, why, why?

ELYOT: Don't ask why. Just give in to me. I swear I'll never ask you to give into me over anything again.

SIBYL [with complete decision]: I won't think of going tonight. It's utterly ridiculous. I've done quite enough travelling for one day, and I'm tired.

ELYOT: You're as obstinate as a mule.

SIBYL: I like that, I must say.

ELYOT [hotly]: You've got your nasty little feet dug into the ground, and you don't intend to budge an inch, do you?

SIBYL [with spirit]: No, I do not.

ELYOT: If there's one thing in the world that infuriates me, it's sheer wanton stubbornness. I should like to cut off your head with a meat axe.

SIBYL: How dare you talk to me like that, on our honeymoon night.

ELYOT: Damn our honeymoon night. Damn it, damn it, damn it!

SIBYL [bursting into tears]: O Elli, Elli—

ELYOT: Stop crying. Will you or will you not come away with me to Paris?

SIBYL: I've never been so miserable in my life. You're hateful and beastly. Mother was perfectly right. She said you had shifty eyes.

59

ELYOT: Well, she can't talk. Hers are so close together, you couldn't put a needle between them.

SIBYL: You don't love me a little bit. I wish I were dead.

ELYOT: Will you or will you not come to Paris?

SIBYL: No, no I won't.

ELYOT: O my God! [*He stamps indoors.*]

SIBYL [*following him, wailing*]: O Elli, Elli, Elli—

[VICTOR *comes stamping out of the french windows on the left, followed by* AMANDA.]

VICTOR: You were certainly right when you said you weren't normal. You're behaving like a lunatic.

AMANDA: Not at all. All I have done is to ask you a little favour.

VICTOR: Little favour indeed.

AMANDA: If we left now we could be in Paris in a few hours.

VICTOR: If we crossed Siberia by train we could be in China in a fortnight, but I don't see any reason to do it.

AMANDA: O Victor darling – please, please – be sensible, just for my sake.

VICTOR: Sensible!

AMANDA: Yes, sensible. I shall be absolutely miserable if we stay here. You don't want me to be absolutely miserable all through my honeymoon, do you?

VICTOR: But why on earth didn't you think of your sister's tragedy before?

AMANDA: I forgot.

VICTOR: You couldn't forget a thing like that.

AMANDA: I got the places muddled. Then when I saw the Casino there in the moonlight, it all came back to me.

VICTOR: When did all this happen?

AMANDA: Years ago, but it might just as well have been yesterday. I can see her now, lying dead, with that dreadful expression on her face. Then all that awful business of taking the body home to England. It was perfectly horrible.

VICTOR: I never knew you had a sister.

AMANDA: I haven't any more.

VICTOR: There's something behind all this.

AMANDA: Don't be silly. What could there be behind it?

VICTOR: Well, for one thing, I know you're lying.

AMANDA: Victor!

VICTOR: Be honest. Aren't you?

AMANDA: I can't think how you can be so mean and suspicious.

VICTOR [*patiently*]: You're lying, Amanda. Aren't you?

AMANDA: Yes, Victor.

VICTOR: You never had a sister, dead or alive?

AMANDA: I believe there was a stillborn one in 1902.

VICTOR: What is your reason for all this?

AMANDA: I told you I was unreliable.

VICTOR: Why do you want to leave so badly?

AMANDA: You'll be angry if I tell you the truth.

VICTOR: What is it?

AMANDA: I warn you.

VICTOR: Tell me. Please tell me.

AMANDA: Elyot's here.

VICTOR: What!

AMANDA: I saw him.

VICTOR: When?

AMANDA: Just now, when you were in the bath.

VICTOR: Where was he?

AMANDA [*hesitatingly*]: Down there, in a white suit. [*She points over the balustrade.*]

VICTOR [*sceptically*]: White suit?

AMANDA: Why not? It's summer, isn't it?

VICTOR: You're lying again.

AMANDA: I'm not. He's here. I swear he is.

VICTOR: Well, what of it?

AMANDA: I can't enjoy a honeymoon with you, with Elyot liable to bounce in at any moment.

VICTOR: Really, Mandy.

AMANDA: Can't you see how awful it is? It's the most embarrassing thing that ever happened to me in my whole life.

VICTOR: Did he see you?

AMANDA: No, he was running.

VICTOR: What was he running for?

AMANDA: How on earth do I know? Don't be so annoying.

VICTOR: Well, as long as he didn't see you it's all right, isn't it?

AMANDA: It isn't all right at all. We must leave immediately.

VICTOR: But why?

AMANDA: How can you be so appallingly obstinate?

VICTOR: I'm not afraid of him.

AMANDA: Neither am I. It isn't a question of being afraid. It's just a horribly awkward situation.

VICTOR: I'm damned if I can see why our whole honeymoon should be upset by Elyot.

AMANDA: My last one was.

VICTOR: I don't believe he's here at all.

AMANDA: He is, I tell you. I saw him.

VICTOR: It was probably an optical illusion. This half light is very deceptive.

AMANDA: It was no such thing.

VICTOR: I absolutely refuse to change all our plans at the last moment, just because you think you've seen Elyot. It's unreasonable and ridiculous of you to demand it. Even if he is here I can't see that it matters. He'll probably feel much more embarrassed than you, and a damned good job too; and if he annoys you in any way I'll knock him down.

AMANDA: That would be charming.

VICTOR: Now don't let's talk about it any more.

AMANDA: Do you mean to stand there seriously and imagine that the whole thing can be glossed over as easily as that?

VICTOR: I'm not going to leave, Mandy. If I start giving in to you as early as this, our lives will be unbearable.

AMANDA [outraged]: Victor!

VICTOR [calmly]: You've worked yourself up into a state over a situation which really only exists in your mind.

AMANDA [controlling herself with an effort]: Please, Victor, please, for this last time I implore you. Let's go to Paris now, tonight. I mean it with all my heart – please—

VICTOR [with gentle firmness]: No, Mandy!

AMANDA: I see quite clearly that I have been foolish enough to marry a fat old gentleman in a club armchair.

VICTOR: It's no use being cross.

AMANDA: You're a pompous ass.

VICTOR [horrified]: Mandy!

AMANDA [enraged]: Pompous ass, that's what I said, and that's what I meant. Blown out with your own importance.

VICTOR: Mandy, control yourself.

AMANDA: Get away from me. I can't bear to think I'm married to such rugged grandeur.

VICTOR [*with great dignity*]: I shall be in the bar. When you are ready to come down and dine, let me know.

AMANDA [*flinging herself into a chair*]: Go away, go away.

[VICTOR *stalks off, at the same moment that* ELYOT *stamps on, on the other side, followed by* SIBYL *in tears.*]

ELYOT: If you don't stop screaming, I'll murder you.

SIBYL: I wish to heaven I'd never seen you in my life, let alone married you. I don't wonder Amanda left you, if you behaved to her as you've behaved to me. I'm going down to have dinner by myself and you can just do what you like about it.

ELYOT: Do, and I hope it chokes you.

SIBYL: O Elli, Elli—

[*She goes wailing indoors.* ELYOT *stamps down to the balustrade and lights a cigarette, obviously trying to control his nerves.* AMANDA *sees him, and comes down too.*]

AMANDA: Give me one, for God's sake.

ELYOT [*hands her his case laconically*]: Here.

AMANDA [*taking a cigarette*]: I'm in such a rage.

ELYOT [*lighting up*]: So am I.

AMANDA: What are we to do?

ELYOT: I don't know.

AMANDA: Whose yacht is that?

ELYOT: The Duke of Westminster's, I expect. It always is.

AMANDA: I wish I were on it.

ELYOT: I wish you were too.

AMANDA: There's no need to be nasty.

ELYOT: Yes there is, every need. I've never in my life felt a greater urge to be nasty.

AMANDA: And you've had some urges in your time, haven't you?

ELYOT: If you start bickering with me, Amanda, I swear I'll throw you over the edge.

AMANDA: Try it, that's all, just try it.

ELYOT: You've upset everything, as usual.

63

AMANDA: I've upset everything! What about you?

ELYOT: Ever since the first moment I was unlucky enough to set eyes on you, my life has been insupportable.

AMANDA: Oh, do shut up, there's no sense in going on like that.

ELYOT: Nothing's any use. There's no escape, ever.

AMANDA: Don't be melodramatic.

ELYOT: Do you want a cocktail? There are two here.

AMANDA: There are two over here as well.

ELYOT: We'll have my two first.

[AMANDA *crosses over into* ELYOT'S *part of the terrace. He gives her one, and keeps one himself.*]

AMANDA: Shall we get roaring screaming drunk?

ELYOT: I don't think that would help; we did it once before and it was a dismal failure.

AMANDA: It was lovely at the beginning.

ELYOT: You have an immoral memory, Amanda. Here's to you. [*They raise their glasses solemnly and drink.*]

AMANDA: I tried to get away the moment after I'd seen you, but he wouldn't budge.

ELYOT: What's his name?

AMANDA: Victor, Victor Prynne.

ELYOT [*toasting*]: Mr and Mrs Victor Prynne. [*He drinks.*] Mine wouldn't budge either.

AMANDA: What's her name?

ELYOT: Sibyl.

AMANDA [*toasting*]: Mr and Mrs Elyot Chase. [*She drinks.*] God pity the poor girl.

ELYOT: Are you in love with him?

AMANDA: Of course.

ELYOT: How funny.

AMANDA: I don't see anything particularly funny about it; you're in love with yours aren't you?

ELYOT: Certainly.

AMANDA: There you are then.

ELYOT: There we both are then.

AMANDA: What's she like?

ELYOT: Fair, very pretty, plays the piano beautifully.

AMANDA: Very comforting.

64

ELYOT: How's yours?

AMANDA: I don't want to discuss him.

ELYOT: Well, it doesn't matter, he'll probably come popping out in a minute and I shall see for myself. Does he know I'm here?

AMANDA: Yes, I told him.

ELYOT [with sarcasm]: That's going to make things a whole lot easier.

AMANDA: You needn't be frightened, he won't hurt you.

ELYOT: If he comes near me I'll scream the place down.

AMANDA: Does Sibyl know I'm here?

ELYOT: No, I pretended I'd had a presentiment. I tried terribly hard to persuade her to leave for Paris.

AMANDA: I tried too. It's lucky we didn't both succeed, isn't it? Otherwise we should probably all have joined up in Rouen or somewhere.

ELYOT [laughing]: In some frowsy little hotel.

AMANDA [laughing too]: Oh dear, it would have been much, much worse.

ELYOT: I can see us all sailing down in the morning for an early start.

AMANDA [weakly]: Lovely, oh lovely.

ELYOT: Glorious!

[They both laugh helplessly.]

AMANDA: What's happened to yours?

ELYOT: Didn't you hear her screaming? She's downstairs in the dining-room, I think.

AMANDA: Mine is being grand, in the bar.

ELYOT: It really is awfully difficult.

AMANDA: Have you known her long?

ELYOT: About four months; we met in a house party in Norfolk.

AMANDA: Very flat, Norfolk.

ELYOT: How old is dear Victor?

AMANDA: Thirty-four, or five; and Sibyl?

ELYOT: I blush to tell you, only twenty-three.

AMANDA: You've gone a mucker all right.

ELYOT: I shall reserve my opinion of your choice until I've met dear Victor.

65

AMANDA: I wish you wouldn't go on calling him 'Dear Victor'. It's extremely irritating.

ELYOT: That's how I see him. Dumpy, and fair, and very considerate, with glasses. Dear Victor.

AMANDA: As I said before, I would rather not discuss him. At least I have good taste enough to refrain from making cheap gibes at Sibyl.

ELYOT: You said Norfolk was flat.

AMANDA: That was no reflection on her, unless she made it flatter.

ELYOT: Your voice takes on an acid quality whenever you mention her name.

AMANDA: I'll never mention it again.

ELYOT: Good, and I'll keep off Victor.

AMANDA [*with dignity*]: Thank you.

[*There is silence for a moment. The orchestra starts playing the same tune that they were singing previously.*]

ELYOT: That orchestra has a remarkably small repertoire.

AMANDA: They don't seem to know anything but this, do they? [*She sits down on the balustrade, and sings it, softly. Her eyes are looking out to sea, and her mind is far away.* ELYOT *watches her while she sings. When she turns to him at the end, there are tears in her eyes. He looks away awkwardly and lights another cigarette.*]

ELYOT: You always had a sweet voice, Amanda.

AMANDA [*a little huskily*]: Thank you.

ELYOT: I'm awfully sorry about all this, really I am. I wouldn't have had it happen for the world.

AMANDA: I know. I'm sorry too. It's just rotten luck.

ELYOT: I'll go away tomorrow whatever happens, so don't you worry.

AMANDA: That's nice of you.

ELYOT: I hope everything turns out splendidly for you, and that you'll be very happy.

AMANDA: I hope the same for you, too. [*The music, which has been playing continually through this little scene, returns persistently to the refrain. They both look at one another and laugh.*]

ELYOT: Nasty insistent little tune.

AMANDA: Strange how potent cheap music is.

ELYOT: What exactly were you remembering at that moment?

AMANDA: The Palace Hotel Skating Rink in the morning, bright strong sunlight, and everybody whirling round in vivid colours, and you kneeling down to put on my skates for me.

ELYOT: You'd fallen on your fanny a few moments before.

AMANDA: It was beastly of you to laugh like that. I felt so humiliated.

ELYOT: Poor darling.

AMANDA: Do you remember waking up in the morning, and standing on the balcony, looking out across the valley?

ELYOT: Blue shadows on white snow, cleanness beyond belief, high above everything in the world. How beautiful it was.

AMANDA: It's nice to think we had a few marvellous moments.

ELYOT: A few: we had heaps really, only they slip away into the background, and one only remembers the bad ones.

AMANDA: Yes. What fools we were to ruin it all. What utter, utter fools.

ELYOT: You feel like that too, do you?

AMANDA [wearily]: Of course.

ELYOT: Why did we?

AMANDA: The whole business was too much for us.

ELYOT: We were so ridiculously over in love.

AMANDA: Funny, wasn't it?

ELYOT [sadly]: Horribly funny.

AMANDA: Selfishness, cruelty, hatred, possessiveness, petty jealousy. All those qualities came out in us just because we loved each other.

ELYOT: Perhaps they were there anyhow.

AMANDA: No, it's love that does it. To hell with love.

ELYOT: To hell with love.

AMANDA: And yet here we are starting afresh with two quite different people. In love all over again, aren't we? [ELYOT doesn't answer.] Aren't we?

ELYOT: No.

AMANDA: Elyot.

ELYOT: We're not in love all over again, and you know it. Goodnight, Amanda. [He turns abruptly, and goes towards the french windows.]

AMANDA: Elyot – don't be silly – come back.

ELYOT: I must go and find Sibyl.

AMANDA: I must go and find Victor.

ELYOT [savagely]: Well, why don't you?

AMANDA: I don't want to.

ELYOT: It's shameful, shameful of us.

AMANDA: Don't: I feel terrible. Don't leave me for a minute, I shall go mad if you do. We won't talk about ourselves any more, we'll talk about outside things, anything you like, only just don't leave me until I've pulled myself together.

ELYOT: Very well.

[There is a dead silence.]

AMANDA: What have you been doing lately? During these last years?

ELYOT: Travelling about. I went round the world, you know, after—

AMANDA [hurriedly]: Yes, yes, I know. How was it?

ELYOT: The world?

AMANDA: Yes.

ELYOT: Oh, highly enjoyable.

AMANDA: China must be very interesting.

ELYOT: Very big, China.

AMANDA: And Japan—

ELYOT: Very small.

AMANDA: Did you eat sharks' fins, and take your shoes off, and use chopsticks and everything?

ELYOT: Practically everything.

AMANDA: And India, the burning ghars, or ghats, or whatever they are, and the Taj Mahal. How was the Taj Mahal?

ELYOT [looking at her]: Unbelievable, a sort of dream.

AMANDA: That was the moonlight, I expect; you must have seen it in the moonlight.

ELYOT [never taking his eyes off her face]: Yes, moonlight is cruelly deceptive.

AMANDA: And it didn't look like a biscuit box, did it? I've always felt that it might.

ELYOT [quietly]: Darling, darling, I love you so.

AMANDA: And I do hope you met a sacred elephant. They're

lint white I believe, and very, very sweet.

ELYOT: I've never loved anyone else for an instant.

AMANDA [*raising her hand feebly in protest*]: No, no, you mustn't – Elyot – stop.

ELYOT: You love me, too, don't you? There's no doubt about it anywhere, is there?

AMANDA: No, no doubt anywhere.

ELYOT: You're looking very lovely, you know, in this damned moonlight. Your skin is clear and cool, and your eyes are shining, and you're growing lovelier and lovelier every second as I look at you. You don't hold any mystery for me, darling, do you mind? There isn't a particle of you that I don't know, remember, and want.

AMANDA [*softly*]: I'm glad, my sweet.

ELYOT: More than any desire anywhere, deep down in my deepest heart I want you back again – please—

AMANDA [*putting her hand over his mouth*]: Don't say any more, you're making me cry so dreadfully.

[*He pulls her gently into his arms and they stand silently, completely oblivious to everything but the moment, and each other. When finally they separate, they sit down, rather breathlessly, on the balustrade.*]

AMANDA: What now? O darling, what now?

ELYOT: I don't know. I'm lost, utterly.

AMANDA: We must think quickly, oh quickly—

ELYOT: Escape?

AMANDA: Together?

ELYOT: Yes, of course, now, now.

AMANDA: We can't, we can't, you know we can't.

ELYOT: We must.

AMANDA: It would break Victor's heart.

ELYOT: And Sibyl's too probably, but they're bound to suffer anyhow. Think of the hell we'd lead them into if we stayed. Infinitely worse than any cruelty in the world, pretending to love them, and loving each other, so desperately.

AMANDA: We must tell them.

ELYOT: What?

AMANDA: Call them, and tell them.

ELYOT: Oh, no, no, that's impossible.

AMANDA: It's honest.

ELYOT: I can't help how honest it is, it's too horrible to think of. How should we start? What should we say?

AMANDA: We should have to trust to the inspiration of the moment.

ELYOT: It would be a moment completely devoid of inspiration. The most appalling moment imaginable. No, no, we can't, you must see that, we simply can't.

AMANDA: What do you propose to do then? As it is, they might appear at any moment.

ELYOT: We've got to decide instantly one way or another. Go away together now, or stay with them, and never see one another again, ever.

AMANDA: Don't be silly, what choice is there?

ELYOT: No choice at all, come— [He takes her hand.]

AMANDA: No, wait. This is sheer raving madness, something's happened to us, we're not sane.

ELYOT: We never were.

AMANDA: Where can we go?

ELYOT: Paris first – my car's in the garage, all ready.

AMANDA: They'll follow us.

ELYOT: That doesn't matter, once the thing's done.

AMANDA: I've got a flat in Paris.

ELYOT: Good.

AMANDA: It's in the Avenue Montaigne. I let it to Freda Lawson, but she's in Biarritz, so it's empty.

ELYOT: Does Victor know?

AMANDA: No, he knows I have one but he hasn't the faintest idea where.

ELYOT: Better and better.

AMANDA: We're being so bad, so terribly bad, we'll suffer for this, I know we shall.

ELYOT: Can't be helped.

AMANDA: Starting all those awful rows all over again.

ELYOT: No, no, we're older and wiser now.

AMANDA: What difference does that make? The first moment either of us gets a bit nervy, off we'll go again.

ELYOT: Stop shilly-shallying, Amanda.

AMANDA: I'm trying to be sensible.

ELYOT: You're only succeeding in being completely idiotic.

AMANDA: Idiotic indeed! What about you?

ELYOT: Now look here, Amanda—

AMANDA [*stricken*]: O my God!

ELYOT [*rushing to her and kissing her*]: Darling, darling, I didn't mean it—

AMANDA: I won't move from here unless we have a compact, a sacred, sacred compact never to quarrel again.

ELYOT: Easy to make but difficult to keep.

AMANDA: No, no, it's the bickering that always starts it. The moment we notice we're bickering, either of us, we must promise on our honour to stop dead. We'll invent some phrase or catchword, which when either of us says it, automatically cuts off all conversation for at least five minutes.

ELYOT: Two minutes dear, with an option of renewal.

AMANDA: Very well, what shall it be?

ELYOT [*hurriedly*]: Solomon Isaacs.

AMANDA: All right, that'll do.

ELYOT: Come on, come on.

AMANDA: What shall we do if we meet either of them on the way downstairs?

ELYOT: Run like stags.

AMANDA: What about clothes?

ELYOT: I've got a couple of bags I haven't unpacked yet.

AMANDA: I've got a small trunk.

ELYOT: Send the porter up for it.

AMANDA: Oh, this is terrible – terrible—

ELYOT: Come on, come on, don't waste time.

AMANDA: Oughtn't we to leave notes or something?

ELYOT: No, no, no, we'll telegraph from somewhere on the road.

AMANDA: Darling, I daren't, it's too wicked of us, I simply daren't.

ELYOT [*seizing her in his arms and kissing her violently*]: Now will you behave?

AMANDA: Yes, but Elyot darling—

ELYOT: Solomon Isaacs!

[*They rush off together through* ELYOT'S *suite. After a moment*

71

or so, VICTOR *steps out on to the terrace and looks round anxiously. Then he goes back indoors again, and can be heard calling* 'MANDY'. *Finally he again comes out on to the terrace and comes despondently down to the balustrade. He hears* SIBYL'S *voice calling* 'ELLI', *and looks round as she comes out of the french windows. She jumps slightly upon seeing him.*]

VICTOR: Good-evening.

SIBYL [*rather flustered*]: Good-evening – I was – er – looking for my husband.

VICTOR: Really, that's funny. I was looking for my wife.

SIBYL: Quite a coincidence. [*She laughs nervously.*]

VICTOR [*after a pause*]: It's very nice here, isn't it?

SIBYL: Lovely.

VICTOR: Have you been here long?

SIBYL: No, we only arrived today.

VICTOR: Another coincidence. So did we.

SIBYL: How awfully funny.

VICTOR: Would you care for a cocktail?

SIBYL: Oh, no thank you – really—

VICTOR: There are two here on the table.

[SIBYL *glances at the two empty glasses on the balustrade, and tosses her head defiantly.*]

SIBYL: Thanks very much, I'd love one.

VICTOR: Good, here you are.

[*Sibyl comes over to Victor's side of the terrace. He hands her one and takes one himself.*]

SIBYL: Thank you.

VICTOR [*with rather forced gaiety*]: To absent friends. [*He raises his glass.*]

SIBYL [*raising hers*]: To absent friends.

[*They both laugh rather mirthlessly and then sit down on the balustrade, pensively sipping their cocktails and looking at the view.*]

It's awfully pretty, isn't it? The moonlight, and the lights of that yacht reflected in the water—

VICTOR: I wonder who it belongs to.

THE CURTAIN SLOWLY FALLS

Act II

The Scene is AMANDA'S *flat in Paris. A few days have elapsed since Act I. The flat is charmingly furnished, its principal features being a Steinway Grand on the Left, facing slightly up stage. Down stage centre, a very large comfortable sofa, behind which is a small table. There is also another sofa somewhere about, and one or two small tables, and a gramophone. The rest can be left to the discretion and taste of the decorator.*

When the curtain rises it is about ten o'clock in the evening. The windows are wide open, and the various street sounds of Paris can be heard, but not very loudly as the apartment is high up.

AMANDA *and* ELYOT *are seated opposite one another at the table. They have finished dinner and are dallying over coffee and liqueurs.* AMANDA *is wearing pyjamas, and* ELYOT *a comfortable dressing-gown.*

AMANDA: I'm glad we let Louise go. I am afraid she is going to have a cold.

ELYOT: Going to have a cold? She's been grunting and snorting all the evening like a whole herd of bison.

AMANDA [*thoughtfully*]: Bison never sounds right to me somehow. I have a feeling it ought to be bisons, a flock of bisons.

ELYOT: You might say a covey of bisons, or even a school of bisons.

AMANDA: Yes, lovely, The Royal London School of Bisons. Do you think Louise is happy at home?

ELYOT: No, profoundly miserable.

AMANDA: Family beastly to her?

ELYOT [*with conviction*]: Absolutely vile. Knock her about dreadfully I expect, make her eat the most disgusting food, and pull her fringe.

AMANDA [*laughing*]: Oh, poor Louise.

ELYOT: Well, you know what the French are.

AMANDA: Oh, yes, indeed. I know what the Hungarians are too.

73

ELYOT: What are they?

AMANDA: Very wistful. It's all those pretzels, I shouldn't wonder.

ELYOT: And the Poostza; I always felt the Poostza was far too big, Danube or no Danube.

AMANDA: Have you ever crossed the Sahara on a camel?

ELYOT: Frequently. When I was a boy we used to do it all the time. My grandmother had a lovely seat on a camel.

AMANDA: There's no doubt about it, foreign travel's the thing.

ELYOT: Would you like some brandy?

AMANDA: Just a little.

[*He pours some into her glass and some into his own.*]

ELYOT: I'm glad we didn't go out tonight.

AMANDA: Or last night.

ELYOT: Or the night before.

AMANDA: There's no reason to, really, when we're cosy here.

ELYOT: Exactly.

AMANDA: It's nice, isn't it?

ELYOT: Strangely peaceful. It's an awfully bad reflection on our characters. We ought to be absolutely tortured with conscience.

AMANDA: We are, every now and then.

ELYOT: Not nearly enough.

AMANDA: We sent Victor and Sibyl a nice note from wherever it was. What more can they want?

ELYOT: You're even more ruthless than I am.

AMANDA: I don't believe in crying over my bridge before I've eaten it.

ELYOT: Very sensible.

AMANDA: Personally, I feel grateful for a miraculous escape. I know now that I should never have been happy with Victor. I was a fool ever to consider it.

ELYOT: You did a little more than consider it.

AMANDA: Well, you can't talk.

ELYOT: I wonder whether they met each other, or whether they've been suffering alone.

AMANDA: Oh dear, don't let's go on about it; it really does make one feel rather awful.

ELYOT: I suppose one or other or both of them will turn up here eventually.

AMANDA: Bound to; it won't be very nice, will it?

ELYOT [*cheerfully*]: Perfectly horrible.

AMANDA: Do you realise that we're living in sin?

ELYOT: Not according to the Catholics. Catholics don't recognise divorce. We're married as much as ever we were.

AMANDA: Yes, dear, but we're not Catholics.

ELYOT: Never mind, it's nice to think they'd sort of back us up. We were married in the eyes of Heaven, and we still are.

AMANDA: We may be all right in the eyes of Heaven, but we look like being in the hell of a mess socially.

ELYOT: Who cares?

AMANDA: Are we going to marry again, after Victor and Sibyl divorce us?

ELYOT: I suppose so. What do you think?

AMANDA: I feel rather scared of marriage really.

ELYOT: It is a frowsy business.

AMANDA: I believe it was just the fact of our being married, and clamped together publicly, that wrecked us before.

ELYOT: That, and not knowing how to manage each other.

AMANDA: Do you think we know how to manage each other now?

ELYOT: This week's been very successful. We've hardly used Solomon Isaacs at all.

AMANDA: Solomon Isaacs is so long, let's shorten it to Sollocks.

ELYOT: All right.

AMANDA: Darling, you do look awfully sweet in your little dressing-gown.

ELYOT: Yes, it's pretty ravishing, isn't it?

AMANDA: Do you mind if I come round and kiss you?

ELYOT: A pleasure, Lady Agatha.

[AMANDA *comes round the table, kisses him, picks up the coffee pot, and returns to her chair.*]

AMANDA: What fools we were to subject ourselves to five years' unnecessary suffering.

ELYOT: Perhaps it wasn't unnecessary, perhaps it mellowed and perfected us like beautiful ripe fruit.

AMANDA: When we were together, did you really think I was unfaithful to you?

ELYOT: Yes, practically every day.

AMANDA: I thought you were too; often I used to torture myself with visions of your bouncing about on divans with awful widows.

ELYOT: Why widows?

AMANDA: I was thinking of Claire Lavenham really.

ELYOT: Oh, Claire.

AMANDA [*sharply*]: What did you say 'Oh, Claire' like that for? It sounded far too careless to me.

ELYOT [*wistfully*]: What a lovely creature she was.

AMANDA: Lovely, lovely, lovely!

ELYOT [*blowing her a kiss*]: Darling!

AMANDA: Did you ever have an affair with her? Afterwards I mean?

ELYOT: Why do you want to know?

AMANDA: Curiosity, I suppose.

ELYOT: Dangerous.

AMANDA: Oh, not now, not dangerous now. I wouldn't expect you to have been celibate during those five years, any more than I was.

ELYOT [*jumping*]: What?

AMANDA: After all, Claire was undeniably attractive. A trifle over vivacious, I always thought, but that was probably because she was fundamentally stupid.

ELYOT: What do you mean about not being celibate during those five years?

AMANDA: What do you think I mean?

ELYOT: O God! [*He looks down miserably.*]

AMANDA: What's the matter?

ELYOT: You know perfectly well what's the matter.

AMANDA [*gently*]: You mustn't be unreasonable. I was only trying to stamp out the memory of you. I expect your affairs well outnumbered mine anyhow.

ELYOT: That is a little different. I'm a man.

AMANDA: Excuse me a moment while I get a caraway biscuit and change my crinoline.

ELYOT: It doesn't suit women to be promiscuous.

AMANDA: It doesn't suit men for women to be promiscuous.

ELYOT [with sarcasm]: Very modern, dear; really, your advanced views quite startle me.

AMANDA: Don't be cross, Elyot. I haven't been so dreadfully loose actually. Five years is a long time, and even if I did nip off with someone every now and again, they were none of them very serious.

ELYOT [rising from the table and walking away]: Oh, do stop it please—

AMANDA: Well, what about you?

ELYOT: Do you want me to tell you?

AMANDA: No, no, I don't – I take everything back – I don't.

ELYOT [viciously]: I was madly in love with a woman in South Africa.

AMANDA: Did she have a ring through her nose?

ELYOT: Don't be revolting.

AMANDA: We're tormenting one another. Sit down, sweet, I'm scared.

ELYOT [slowly]: Very well. [He sits down thoughtfully.]

AMANDA: We should have said Sollocks ages ago.

ELYOT: We're in love all right.

AMANDA: Don't say it so bitterly. Let's try to get the best out of it this time, instead of the worst.

ELYOT [stretching his hand across the table]: Hand, please.

AMANDA [clasping it]: Here.

ELYOT: More comfortable?

AMANDA: Much more.

ELYOT [after a slight pause]: Are you engaged for this dance?

AMANDA: Funnily enough I was, but my partner was suddenly taken ill.

ELYOT [rising and going to the gramophone]: It's this damned smallpox epidemic.

AMANDA: No, as a matter of fact it was kidney trouble.

ELYOT: You'll dance it with me, I hope?

AMANDA [rising]: I shall be charmed.

ELYOT [as they dance]: Quite a good floor, isn't it?

AMANDA: Yes, I think it needs a little Borax.

77

ELYOT: I love Borax.

AMANDA: Is that the Grand Duchess Olga lying under the piano?

ELYOT: Yes, her husband died a few weeks ago, you know, on his way back from Pulborough. So sad.

AMANDA: What on earth was he doing in Pulborough?

ELYOT: Nobody knows exactly, but there have been the usual stories.

AMANDA: I see.

ELYOT: Delightful parties Lady Bundle always gives, doesn't she?

AMANDA: Entrancing. Such a dear old lady.

ELYOT: And so gay. Did you notice her at supper blowing all those shrimps through her ear trumpet?

[*The tune comes to an end.* AMANDA *sits on the edge of the sofa, pensively.*]

ELYOT: What are you thinking about?

AMANDA: Nothing in particular.

ELYOT: Come on, I know that face.

AMANDA: Poor Sibyl.

ELYOT: Sibyl?

AMANDA: Yes, I suppose she loves you terribly.

ELYOT: Not as much as all that; she didn't have a chance to get really under way.

AMANDA: I expect she's dreadfully unhappy.

ELYOT: Oh, do shut up, Amanda, we've had all that out before.

AMANDA: We've certainly been pretty busy trying to justify ourselves.

ELYOT: It isn't a question of justifying ourselves, it's the true values of the situation that are really important. The moment we saw one another again we knew it was no use going on. We knew it instantly really, although we tried to pretend to ourselves that we didn't. What we've got to be thankful for is that we made the break straight away, and not later.

AMANDA: You think we should have done it anyhow?

ELYOT: Of course, and things would have been in a worse mess than they are now.

AMANDA: And what if we'd never happened to meet again?

78

Would you have been quite happy with Sibyl?

ELYOT: I expect so.

AMANDA: O Elyot!

ELYOT: You needn't look so stricken. It would have been the same with you and Victor. Life would have been smooth, and amicable, and quite charming, wouldn't it?

AMANDA: Poor dear Victor. He certainly did love me.

ELYOT: Splendid.

AMANDA: When I met him I was so lonely and depressed, I felt that I was getting old, and crumbling away unwanted.

ELYOT: It certainly is horrid when one begins to crumble.

AMANDA [wistfully]: He used to look at me hopelessly, like a lovely spaniel, and I sort of melted like snow in the sunlight.

ELYOT: That must have been an edifying spectacle.

AMANDA: Victor really had a great charm.

ELYOT: You must tell me all about it.

AMANDA: He had a positive mania for looking after me, and protecting me.

ELYOT: That would have died down in time, dear.

AMANDA: You mustn't be rude, there's no necessity to be rude.

ELYOT: I wasn't in the least rude, I merely made a perfectly rational statement.

AMANDA: Your voice was decidedly bitter.

ELYOT: Victor had glorious legs, hadn't he? And fascinating ears.

AMANDA: Don't be silly.

ELYOT: He probably looked radiant in the morning, all flushed and tumbled on the pillow.

AMANDA: I never saw him on the pillow.

ELYOT: I'm surprised to hear it.

AMANDA [angrily]: Elyot!

ELYOT: There's no need to be cross.

AMANDA: What did you mean by that?

ELYOT: I'm sick of listening to you yap, yap, yap, yap, yap, yapping about Victor.

AMANDA: Now listen Elyot, once and for all—

ELYOT: O my dear, Sollocks! Sollocks! – two minutes – Sollocks.

79

AMANDA: But—

ELYOT [firmly]: Sollocks!

[They sit in dead silence, looking at each other. AMANDA makes
a sign that she wants a cigarette. ELYOT gets up, hands her the
box, and lights one for her and himself. AMANDA rises and
walks over to the window, and stands there, looking out for a
moment. Presently ELYOT joins her. She slips her arm through
his, and they kiss lightly. They draw the curtains and then come
down and sit side by side on the sofa. ELYOT looks at his watch.
AMANDA raises her eyebrows at him and he nods, then they
both sigh, audibly.]

That was a near thing.

AMANDA: It was my fault. I'm terribly sorry, darling.

ELYOT: I was very irritating, I know I was. I'm sure Victor was
awfully nice, and you're perfectly right to be sweet about him.

AMANDA: That's downright handsome of you. Sweetheart!
[She kisses him.]

ELYOT [leaning back with her on the sofa]: I think I love you more
than ever before. Isn't it ridiculous? Put your feet up.

[She puts her legs across his, and they snuggle back together in
the corner of the sofa, his head resting on her shoulder.]

AMANDA: Comfortable?

ELYOT: Almost, wait a minute. [He struggles a bit and then settles
down with a sigh.]

AMANDA: How long, O Lord, how long?

ELYOT [drowsily]: What do you mean, 'How long, O Lord, how
long?'

AMANDA: This is far too perfect to last.

ELYOT: You have no faith, that's what's wrong with you.

AMANDA: Absolutely none.

ELYOT: Don't you believe in—? [He nods upwards.]

AMANDA: No, do you?

ELYOT [shaking his head]: No. What about—? [He points down-
wards.]

AMANDA: Oh dear, no.

ELYOT: Don't you believe in anything?

AMANDA: Oh, yes, I believe in being kind to everyone, and giving money to old beggar women, and being as gay as possible.

ELYOT: What about after we're dead?

AMANDA: I think a rather gloomy merging into everything, don't you?

ELYOT: I hope not; I'm a bad merger.

AMANDA: You won't know a thing about it.

ELYOT: I hope for a glorious oblivion, like being under gas.

AMANDA: I always dream the most peculiar things under gas.

ELYOT: Would you be young always? If you could choose?

AMANDA: No, I don't think so, not if it meant having awful bull's glands popped into me.

ELYOT: Cows for you dear. Bulls for me.

AMANDA: We certainly live in a marvellous age.

ELYOT: Too marvellous. It's all right if you happen to be a specialist at something, then you're too concentrated to pay attention to all the other things going on. But, for the ordinary observer, it's too much.

AMANDA [snuggling closer]: Far, far too much.

ELYOT: Take the radio for instance.

AMANDA: O darling, don't let's take the radio.

ELYOT: Well, aeroplanes then, and cosmic atoms, and television, and those gland injections we were talking about just now.

AMANDA: It must be so nasty for the poor animals, being experimented on.

ELYOT: Not when the experiments are successful. Why, in Vienna I believe you can see whole lines of decrepit old rats carrying on like Tiller Girls.

AMANDA [laughing]: Oh, how very, very sweet.

ELYOT [burying his face in her shoulder]: I do love you so.

AMANDA: Don't blow, dear heart, it gives me the shivers.

ELYOT [trying to kiss her]: Swivel your face round a bit more.

AMANDA [obliging]: That better?

ELYOT [kissing her lingeringly]: Very nice, thank you kindly.

AMANDA [twining her arms round his neck]: Darling, you're so terribly, terribly dear, and sweet, and attractive. [She pulls his head down to her again and they kiss lovingly.]

ELYOT [softly]: We were raving mad, ever to part, even for an instant.

AMANDA: Utter imbeciles.

ELYOT: I realised it almost immediately, didn't you?

AMANDA: Long before we got our decree.

ELYOT: My heart broke on that damned trip round the world. I saw such beautiful things, darling. Moonlight shining on old temples, strange barbaric dances in jungle villages, scarlet flamingoes flying over deep, deep blue water. Breathlessly lovely, and completely unexciting because you weren't there to see them with me.

AMANDA [kissing him again]: Take me please, take me at once, let's make up for lost time.

ELYOT: Next week?

AMANDA: Tomorrow.

ELYOT: Done.

AMANDA: I must see those dear flamingoes. [There is a pause.] Eight years all told, we've loved each other. Three married and five divorced.

ELYOT: Angel. Angel. Angel. [He kisses her passionately.]

AMANDA [struggling slightly]: No, Elyot, stop now, stop—

ELYOT: Why should I stop? You know you adore being made love to.

AMANDA [through his kisses]: It's so soon after dinner.

ELYOT [jumping up rather angrily]: You really do say most awful things.

AMANDA [tidying her hair]: I don't see anything particularly awful about that.

ELYOT: No sense of glamour, no sense of glamour at all.

AMANDA: It's difficult to feel really glamorous with a crick in the neck.

ELYOT: Why didn't you say you had a crick in your neck?

AMANDA [sweetly]: It's gone now.

ELYOT: How convenient. [He lights a cigarette.]

AMANDA [holding out her hand]: I want one please.

ELYOT [throwing her one]: Here.

AMANDA: Match?

ELYOT [impatiently]: Wait a minute, can't you?

AMANDA: Chivalrous little love.

ELYOT [throwing the matches at her]: Here.

AMANDA [coldly]: Thank you very much indeed.
[There is a silence for a moment.]
ELYOT: You really can be more irritating than anyone in the world.
AMANDA: I fail to see what I've done that's so terribly irritating.
ELYOT: You have no tact.
AMANDA: Tact. You have no consideration.
ELYOT [walking up and down]: Too soon after dinner, indeed.
AMANDA: Yes, much too soon.
ELYOT: That sort of remark shows rather a common sort of mind, I'm afraid.
AMANDA: Oh, it does, does it?
ELYOT: Very unpleasant, makes me shudder.
AMANDA: Making all this fuss just because your silly vanity is a little upset.
ELYOT: Vanity? What do you mean, vanity?
AMANDA: You can't bear the thought that there are certain moments when our chemical what d'you call 'ems don't fuse properly.
ELYOT [derisively]: Chemical what d'you call 'ems? Please try to be more explicit.
AMANDA: You know perfectly well what I mean, and don't you try to patronise me.
ELYOT [loudly]: Now look here, Amanda—
AMANDA [suddenly]: Darling, Sollocks! Oh, for God's sake, Sollocks!
ELYOT: But listen—
AMANDA: Sollocks, Sollocks. Oh dear – triple Sollocks!
[They stand looking at one another in silence for a moment, then AMANDA flings herself down on the sofa and buries her face in the cushions. ELYOT looks at her, then goes over to the piano. He sits down and begins to play idly. AMANDA raises her head, screws herself round on the sofa, and lies there listening. ELYOT blows a kiss to her and goes on playing. He starts to sing softly to her, never taking his eyes off her. When he has finished the little refrain, whatever it was, he still continues to play it, looking at her.]
AMANDA: Big romantic stuff, darling.
ELYOT [smiling]: Yes, big romantic stuff.

[*He wanders off into another tune.* AMANDA *sits up cross-legged on the sofa, and begins to sing it, then, still singing, she comes over and perches on the piano. They sing several old refrains from dead and gone musical comedies, finishing with the song that brought them together again in the first Act. Finally* AMANDA *comes down and sits next to him on the piano stool; they both therefore have their backs half turned to the audience. She rests her head on his shoulder, until finally his fingers drop off the keys, and they melt into one another's arms.*]

ELYOT [*after a moment*]: You're the most thrilling, exciting woman that was ever born.

AMANDA [*standing up, and brushing her hand lightly over his mouth*]: Dearest, dearest heart—

[*He catches at her hand and kisses it, and then her arm, until he is standing up, embracing her ardently. She struggles a little, half laughing, and breaks away, but he catches her, and they finish up on the sofa again, clasped in each other's arms, both completely given up to the passion of the moment, until the telephone bell rings violently, and they both spring apart.*]

ELYOT: Good God!

AMANDA: Do you think it's them?

ELYOT: I wonder.

AMANDA: Nobody knows we're here except Freda, and she wouldn't ring up.

ELYOT: It must be them then.

AMANDA: What are we to do?

ELYOT [*suddenly*]: We're all right darling, aren't we – whatever happens?

AMANDA: Now and always, sweet.

ELYOT: I don't care then.

[*He gets up and goes defiantly over to the telephone, which has been ringing incessantly during the little preceding scene.*]

AMANDA: It was bound to come sooner or later.

ELYOT [*at telephone*]: Hallo – hallo – what – comment? Madame, qui? 'allo – 'allo – oui, c'est ça. Oh, Madame Duvallon – Oui, oui, oui. [*He puts his hand over the mouthpiece.*] It's only somebody wanting to talk to the dear Madame Duvallon.

AMANDA: Who's she?

ELYOT: I haven't the faintest idea. [*At telephone*] Je regrette beau-
coup Monsieur, mais Madame Duvallon viens de partir –
cette apres midi, pour Madagascar. [*He hangs up the telephone.*]
Whew; that gave me a fright.

AMANDA: It sent shivers up my spine.

ELYOT: What shall we do if they suddenly walk in on us?

AMANDA: Behave exquisitely.

ELYOT: With the most perfect poise?

AMANDA: Certainly. I shall probably do a court curtsey.

ELYOT [*sitting on the edge of the sofa*]: Things that ought to matter
dreadfully, don't matter at all when one's happy, do they?

AMANDA: What is so horrible is that one can't stay happy.

ELYOT: Darling, don't say that.

AMANDA: It's true. The whole business is a very poor joke.

ELYOT: Meaning that sacred and beautiful thing, Love?

AMANDA: Yes, meaning just that.

ELYOT [*striding up and down the room dramatically*]: What does it
all mean, that's what I ask myself in my ceaseless quest for
ultimate truth. Dear God, what does it all mean?

AMANDA: Don't laugh at me, I'm serious.

ELYOT [*seriously*]: You mustn't be serious, my dear one, it's just
what they want.

AMANDA: Who's they?

ELYOT: All the futile moralists who try to make life unbearable.
Laugh at them. Be flippant. Laugh at everything, all their
sacred shibboleths. Flippancy brings out the acid in their
damned sweetness and light.

AMANDA: If I laugh at everything, I must laugh at us too.

ELYOT: Certainly you must. We're figures of fun, all right.

AMANDA: How long will it last, this ludicrous, overbearing love
of ours?

ELYOT: Who knows?

AMANDA: Shall we always want to bicker and fight?

ELYOT: No, that desire will fade, along with our passion.

AMANDA: Oh dear, shall we like that?

ELYOT: It all depends on how well we've played.

AMANDA: What happens if one of us dies? Does the one that's
left still laugh?

ELYOT: Yes, yes, with all his might.

AMANDA [*wistfully clutching his hand*]: That's serious enough, isn't it?

ELYOT: No, no, it isn't. Death's very laughable, such a cunning little mystery. All done with mirrors.

AMANDA: Darling, I believe you're talking nonsense.

ELYOT: So is everyone else in the long run. Let's be superficial and pity the poor philosophers. Let's blow trumpets and squeakers, and enjoy the party as much as we can, like very small, quite idiotic school-children. Let's savour the delight of the moment. Come and kiss me, darling, before your body rots, and worms pop in and out of your eye sockets.

AMANDA: Elyot, worms don't pop.

ELYOT [*kissing her*]: I don't mind what you do, see? You can paint yourself bright green all over, and dance naked in the Place Vendôme, and rush off madly with all the men in the world, and I shan't say a word, as long as you love me best.

AMANDA: Thank you, dear. The same applies to you, except that if I catch you so much as looking at another woman, I'll kill you.

ELYOT: Do you remember that awful scene we had in Venice?

AMANDA: Which particular one?

ELYOT: The one when you bought that little painted wooden snake on the Piazza, and put it on my bed.

AMANDA: Oh, Charles. That was his name, Charles. He did wriggle so beautifully.

ELYOT: Horrible thing, I hated it.

AMANDA: Yes, I know you did. You threw it out of the window into the Grand Canal. I don't think I'll ever forgive you for that.

ELYOT: How long did the row last?

AMANDA: It went on intermittently for days.

ELYOT: The worst one was in Cannes when your curling irons burnt a hole in my new dressing-gown. [*He laughs.*]

AMANDA: It burnt my comb too, and all the towels in the bathroom.

ELYOT: That was a rouser, wasn't it?

AMANDA: That was the first time you ever hit me.

86

ELYOT: I didn't hit you very hard.

AMANDA: The manager came in and found us rolling on the floor, biting and scratching like panthers. Oh dear, oh dear – [*She laughs helplessly.*]

ELYOT: I shall never forget his face.

[*They both collapse with laughter.*]

AMANDA: How ridiculous, how utterly, utterly ridiculous.

ELYOT: We were very much younger then.

AMANDA: And very much sillier.

ELYOT: As a matter of fact, the real cause of that row was Peter Burden.

AMANDA: You knew there was nothing in that.

ELYOT: I didn't know anything of the sort; you took presents from him.

AMANDA: Presents: only a trivial little brooch.

ELYOT: I remember it well, bristling with diamonds. In the worst possible taste.

AMANDA: Not at all, it was very pretty. I still have it, and I wear it often.

ELYOT: You went out of your way to torture me over Peter Burden.

AMANDA: No, I didn't, you worked the whole thing up in your jealous imagination.

ELYOT: You must admit that he was in love with you, wasn't he?

AMANDA: Just a little, perhaps. Nothing serious.

ELYOT: You let him kiss you. You said you did.

AMANDA: Well, what of it?

ELYOT: What of it!

AMANDA: It gave him a lot of pleasure, and it didn't hurt me.

ELYOT: What about me?

AMANDA: If you hadn't been so suspicious and nosey you'd never have known a thing about it.

ELYOT: That's a nice point of view, I must say.

AMANDA: Oh dear, I'm bored with this conversation.

ELYOT: So am I, bored stiff. [*He goes over to the table.*] Want some brandy?

AMANDA: No thanks.

ELYOT: I'll have a little, I think.

AMANDA: I don't see why you want it, you've already had two
glasses.

ELYOT: No particular reason; anyhow they were very small
ones.

AMANDA: It seems so silly to go on, and on, and on with a thing.

ELYOT [*pouring himself out a glassful*]: You can hardly call three
liqueur glasses in a whole evening going on, and on, and on.

AMANDA: It's become a habit with you.

ELYOT: You needn't be so grand, just because you don't happen
to want any yourself at the moment.

AMANDA: Don't be so stupid.

ELYOT [*irritably*]: Really, Amanda—

AMANDA: What?

ELYOT: Nothing.

[AMANDA *sits down on the sofa, and, taking a small mirror
from her bag, gazes at her face critically, and then uses some lipstick and powder. A trifle nastily.*]

Going out somewhere dear?

AMANDA: No, just making myself fascinating for you.

ELYOT: That reply has broken my heart.

AMANDA: The woman's job is to allure the man. Watch me a
minute, will you?

ELYOT: As a matter of fact that's perfectly true.

AMANDA: Oh, no, it isn't.

ELYOT: Yes it is.

AMANDA [*snappily*]: Oh, be quiet.

ELYOT: It's a pity you didn't have any more brandy; it might
have made you a little less disagreeable.

AMANDA: It doesn't seem to have worked such wonders with
you.

ELYOT: Snap, snap, snap; like a little adder.

AMANDA: Adders don't snap, they sting.

ELYOT: Nonsense, they have a little bag of venom behind their
fangs and they snap.

AMANDA: They sting.

ELYOT: They snap.

AMANDA [*with exasperation*]: I don't care, do you understand? I
don't care. I don't mind if they bark, and roll about like hoops.

ELYOT [after a slight pause]: Did you see much of Peter Burden after our divorce?

AMANDA: Yes, I did, quite a lot.

ELYOT: I suppose you let him kiss you a good deal more then.

AMANDA: Mind your own business.

ELYOT: You must have had a riotous time. [AMANDA doesn't answer, so he stalks about the room.] No restraint at all – very enjoyable – you never had much anyhow.

AMANDA: You're quite insufferable; I expect it's because you're drunk.

ELYOT: I'm not in the least drunk.

AMANDA: You always had a weak head.

ELYOT: I think I mentioned once before that I have only had three minute liqueur glasses of brandy the whole evening long. A child of two couldn't get drunk on that.

AMANDA: On the contrary, a child of two could get violently drunk on only one glass of brandy.

ELYOT: Very interesting. How about a child of four, and a child of six, and a child of nine?

AMANDA [turning her head away]: Oh, do shut up.

ELYOT [witheringly]: We might get up a splendid little debate about that, you know: Intemperate Tots.

AMANDA: Not very funny, dear; you'd better have some more brandy.

ELYOT: Very good idea, I will. [He pours out another glass and gulps it down defiantly.]

AMANDA: Ridiculous ass.

ELYOT: I beg your pardon?

AMANDA: I said ridiculous ass!

ELYOT [with great dignity]: Thank you.

[There is a silence. AMANDA gets up, and turns the gramophone on.]

You'd better turn that off, I think.

AMANDA [coldly]: Why?

ELYOT: It's very late and it will annoy the people upstairs.

AMANDA: There aren't any people upstairs. It's a photographer's studio.

ELYOT: There are people downstairs, I suppose?

AMANDA: They're away in Tunis.

ELYOT: This is no time of the year for Tunis. [*He turns the gramophone off.*]

AMANDA [*icily*]: Turn it on again, please.

ELYOT: I'll do no such thing.

AMANDA: Very well, if you insist on being boorish and idiotic. [*She gets up and turns it on again.*]

ELYOT: Turn it off. It's driving me mad.

AMANDA: You're far too temperamental. Try to control yourself.

ELYOT: Turn it off.

AMANDA: I won't.

> [ELYOT *rushes at the gramophone.* AMANDA *tries to ward him off. They struggle silently for a moment, then the needle screeches across the record.*]

There now, you've ruined the record. [*She takes it off and scrutinises it.*]

ELYOT: Good job, too.

AMANDA: Disagreeable pig.

ELYOT [*suddenly stricken with remorse*]: Amanda darling – Sollocks.

AMANDA [*furiously*]: Sollocks yourself. [*She breaks the record over his head.*]

ELYOT [*staggering*]: You spiteful little beast.

> [*He slaps her face. She screams loudly and hurls herself sobbing with rage on to the sofa, with her face buried in the cushions.*]

AMANDA [*wailing*]: Oh, oh, oh—

ELYOT: I'm sorry, I didn't mean it – I'm sorry, darling, I swear I didn't mean it.

AMANDA: Go away, go away, I hate you.

> [ELYOT *kneels on the sofa and tries to pull her round to look at him.*]

ELYOT: Amanda – listen – listen—

AMANDA [*turning suddenly, and fetching him a welt across the face*]: Listen indeed; I'm sick and tired of listening to you, you damned sadistic bully.

ELYOT [*with great grandeur*]: Thank you

> [*He stalks towards the door, in stately silence.* AMANDA *throws a cushion at him, which misses him and knocks down a lamp*

and a vase on the side table. ELYOT *laughs falsely.*]
A pretty display, I must say.

AMANDA [*wildly*]: Stop laughing like that.

ELYOT [*continuing*]: Very amusing indeed.

AMANDA [*losing control*]: Stop – stop – stop – [*She rushes at him, he grabs her hands and they sway about the room, until he manages to twist her round by the arms so that she faces him, closely, quivering with fury.*] – I hate you – do you hear? You're conceited, and overbearing, and utterly impossible!

ELYOT [*shouting her down*]: You're a vile-tempered loose-living wicked little beast, and I never want to see you again so long as I live.

[*He flings her away from him, she staggers, and falls against a chair. They stand gasping at one another in silence for a moment.*]

AMANDA [*very quietly*]: This is the end, do you understand? The end, finally and for ever.

[*She goes to the door, which opens on to the landing, and wrenches it open. He rushes after her and clutches her wrist.*]

ELYOT: You're not going like this.

AMANDA: Oh, yes I am.

ELYOT: You're not.

AMANDA: I am; let go of me—

[*He pulls her away from the door, and once more they struggle. This time a standard lamp crashes to the ground.* AMANDA, *breathlessly, as they fight*]

You're a cruel fiend, and I hate and loathe you; thank God I've realised in time what you're really like; marry you again, never, never, never . . . I'd rather die in torment—

ELYOT [*at the same time*]: Shut up; shut up. I wouldn't marry you again if you came crawling to me on your bended knees. You're a mean, evil minded, little vampire – I hope to God I never set eyes on you again as long as I live—

[*At this point in the proceedings they trip over a piece of carpet, and fall on to the floor, rolling over and over in paroxysms of rage.* VICTOR *and* SIBYL *enter quietly, through the open door, and stand staring at them in horror. Finally* AMANDA *breaks free and half gets up,* ELYOT *grabs her leg, and she falls against a table, knocking it completely over.*]

AMANDA [*screaming*]: Beast; brute; swine; cad; beast; beast; brute; devil—

[*She rushes back at* ELYOT *who is just rising to his feet, and gives him a stinging blow, which knocks him over again. She rushes blindly off Left, and slams the door, at the same moment that he jumps up and rushes off Right, also slamming the door.* VICTOR *and* SIBYL *advance apprehensively into the room, and sink on to the sofa—*]

THE CURTAIN FALLS

Act III

The Scene is the same as Act II. It is the next morning. The time is about eight-thirty. VICTOR *and* SIBYL *have drawn the two sofas across the doors Right, and Left, and are stretched on them, asleep.* VICTOR *is in front of* AMANDA'S *door, and* SIBYL *in front of* ELYOT'S.

The room is in chaos, as it was left the night before.

As the curtain rises, there is the rattling of a key in the lock of the front door, and LOUISE *enters. She is rather a frowsy looking girl, and carries a string bag with various bundles of eatables crammed into it, notably a long roll of bread and a lettuce. She closes the door after her, and in the half light trips over the standard lamp lying on the floor. She puts her string bag down, and gropes her way over to the window. She draws the curtains, letting sunlight stream into the room. When she looks round, she gives a little cry of horror. Then she sees* VICTOR *and* SIBYL *sleeping peacefully, and comes over and scrutinises each of them with care, then she shakes* SIBYL *by the shoulder.*

SIBYL [*waking*]: Oh dear.

LOUISE: Bonjour, Madame.

SIBYL [*bewildered*]: What? – Oh – bonjour.

LOUISE: Qu'est-ce que vous faites ici, Madame?

SIBYL: What – what? – Wait a moment, attendez un instant – oh dear—

VICTOR [*sleepily*]: What's happening? [*Jumping up*] Of course, I remember now. [*He sees* LOUISE.] Oh!

LOUISE [*firmly*]: Bonjour, Monsieur.

VICTOR: Er – bonjour – What time is it?

LOUISE [*rather dully*]: Eh, Monsieur?

SIBYL [*sitting up on the sofa*]: Quelle heure est-il, s'il vous plait?

LOUISE: C'est neuf heure moins dix, madame.

VICTOR: What did she say?

SIBYL: I think she said nearly ten o'clock.

VICTOR [*taking situation in hand*]: Er – voulez – er – wake – revillez Monsieur et Madame – er – toute suite?

LOUISE [*shaking her head*]: Non, Monsieur. Il m'est absolument defendu de les appeler jusqu'à ce qu'ils sonnent.

[*She takes her bag and goes off into the kitchen.* VICTOR *and* SIBYL *look at each other helplessly.*]

SIBYL: What are we to do?

VICTOR [*with determination*]: Wake them ourselves. [*He goes towards* AMANDA'S *door.*]

SIBYL: No, no, wait a minute.

VICTOR: What's the matter?

SIBYL [*plaintively*]: I couldn't face them yet, really, I couldn't; I feel dreadful.

VICTOR: So do I. [*He wanders gloomily over to the window.*] It's a lovely morning.

SIBYL: Lovely. [*She bursts into tears.*]

VICTOR [*coming to her*]: I say, don't cry.

SIBYL: I can't help it.

VICTOR: Please don't, please—

SIBYL: It's all so squalid, I wish we hadn't stayed; what's the use?

VICTOR: We've got to see them before we go back to England. We must get things straightened out.

SIBYL [*sinking down on to the sofa*]: Oh dear, oh dear, oh dear, I wish I were dead.

VICTOR: Hush, now, hush. Remember your promise. We've got to see this through together and get it settled one way or another.

SIBYL [*sniffling*]: I'll try to control myself, only I'm so . . . so tired, I haven't slept properly for ages.

VICTOR: Neither have I.

SIBYL: If we hadn't arrived when we did, they'd have killed one another.

VICTOR: They must have been drunk.

SIBYL: She hit him.

VICTOR: He'd probably hit her, too, earlier on.

SIBYL: I'd no idea anyone ever behaved like that; it's so disgusting, so degrading. Elli of all people – oh dear— [*She almost breaks down again, but controls herself.*]

VICTOR: What an escape you've had.

SIBYL: What an escape we've both had.

[AMANDA *opens her door and looks out. She is wearing travelling clothes, and is carrying a small suitcase. She jumps, upon seeing* SIBYL *and* VICTOR.]

AMANDA: Oh! – good-morning.

VICTOR [*with infinite reproach in his voice*]: Oh, Amanda.

AMANDA: Will you please move this sofa, I can't get out.

[VICTOR *moves the sofa, and she advances into the room and goes towards the door.*]

VICTOR: Where are you going?

AMANDA: Away.

VICTOR: You can't.

AMANDA: Why not?

VICTOR: I want to talk to you.

AMANDA [*wearily*]: What on earth is the use of that?

VICTOR: I must talk to you.

AMANDA: Well, all I can say is, it's very inconsiderate. [*She plumps the bag down by the door and comes down to* VICTOR.]

VICTOR: Mandy, I—

AMANDA [*gracefully determined to rise above the situation*]: I suppose you're Sibyl; how do you do? [SIBYL *turns her back on her.*] Well, if you're going to take up that attitude, I fail to see the point of your coming here at all.

SIBYL: I came to see Elyot.

AMANDA: I've no wish to prevent you. He's in there, probably wallowing in an alcoholic stupor.

VICTOR: This is all very unpleasant, Amanda.

AMANDA: I quite agree, that's why I want to go away.

VICTOR: That would be shirking; this must be discussed at length.

AMANDA: Very well, if you insist, but not just now, I don't feel up to it. Has Louise come yet?

VICTOR: If Louise is the maid, she's in the kitchen.

AMANDA: Thank you. You'd probably like some coffee; excuse me a moment. [*She goes off into the kitchen.*]

SIBYL: Well! How dare she?

VICTOR [*irritably*]: How dare she what?

SIBYL: Behave so calmly, as though nothing had happened.

VICTOR: I don't see what else she could have done.

SIBYL: Insufferable, I call it.

[ELYOT *opens his door and looks out.*]

ELYOT [*seeing them*]: O God. [*He shuts the door again quickly.*]

SIBYL: Elyot – Elyot— [*She rushes over to the door and bangs on it.*] Elyot – Elyot – Elyot—

ELYOT [*inside*]: Go away.

SIBYL [*falling on to the sofa*]: Oh, oh, oh. [*She bursts into tears again.*]

VICTOR: Do pull yourself together, for Heaven's sake.

SIBYL: I can't, I can't – oh, oh, oh—

[AMANDA *re-enters.*]

AMANDA: I've ordered some coffee and rolls, they'll be here soon. I must apologise for the room being so untidy.

[*She picks up a cushion, and pats it into place on the sofa. There is a silence except for* SIBYL'S *sobs.* AMANDA *looks at her, and then at* VICTOR; *then she goes off into her room again, and shuts the door.*]

VICTOR: It's no use crying like that, it doesn't do any good.

[*After a moment, during which* SIBYL *makes renewed efforts to control her tears,* ELYOT *opens the door immediately behind her, pushes the sofa, with her on it, out of the way, and walks towards the front door. He is in travelling clothes, and carrying a small suitcase.*]

SIBYL [*rushing after him*]: Elyot, where are you going?

ELYOT: Canada.

SIBYL: You can't go like this, you can't.

ELYOT: I see no point in staying.

VICTOR: You owe it to Sibyl to stay.

ELYOT: How do you do, I don't think we've met before.

SIBYL: You must stay, you've got to stay.

ELYOT: Very well, if you insist. [*He plumps his bag down.*] I'm afraid the room is in rather a mess. Have you seen the maid Louise?

VICTOR: She's in the kitchen.

ELYOT: Good. I'll order some coffee. [*He makes a movement towards the kitchen.*]

VICTOR [*stopping him*]: No, your – er – my – er – Amanda has already ordered it.

ELYOT: Oh, I'm glad the old girl's up and about.

VICTOR: We've got to get things straightened out, you know.

ELYOT [*looking around the room*]: Yes, it's pretty awful. We'll get the concierge up from downstairs.

VICTOR: You're being purposely flippant, but it's no good.

ELYOT: Sorry. [*He lapses into silence.*]

VICTOR [*after a pause*]: What's to be done?

ELYOT: I don't know.

SIBYL [*with spirit*]: It's all perfectly horrible. I feel smirched and unclean as though slimy things had been crawling all over me.

ELYOT: Maybe they have; that's a very old sofa.

VICTOR: If you don't stop your damned flippancy, I'll knock your head off.

ELYOT [*raising his eyebrows*]: Has it ever struck you that flippancy might cover a very real embarrassment?

VICTOR: In a situation such as this, it's in extremely bad taste.

ELYOT: No worse than bluster, and invective. As a matter of fact, as far as I know, this situation is entirely without precedent. We have no prescribed etiquette to fall back upon. I shall continue to be flippant.

SIBYL: O Elyot, how can you – how can you.

ELYOT: I'm awfully sorry, Sibyl.

VICTOR: It's easy enough to be sorry.

ELYOT: On the contrary. I find it exceedingly difficult. I seldom regret anything. This is a very rare and notable exception, a sort of Red Letter Day. We must all make the most of it.

SIBYL: I'll never forgive you, never. I wouldn't have believed anyone could be so callous and cruel.

ELYOT: I absolutely see your point, and as I said before, I'm sorry.

[*There is silence for a moment. Then* AMANDA *comes in again. She has obviously decided to carry everything off in a high-handed manner.*]

AMANDA [*in social tones*]: What! Breakfast not ready yet? Really, these French servants are too slow for words. [*She smiles gaily.*] What a glorious morning. [*She goes to the window.*] I do love Paris, it's so genuinely gay. Those lovely trees in the Champs Elysées, and the little roundabouts for the children to play on, and those shiny red taxis. You can see Sacré Coeur quite clearly today. Sometimes it's a bit misty, particularly in August, all the heat rising up from the pavements, you know.

ELYOT [*drily*]: Yes, dear, we know.

AMANDA [*ignoring him*]: And it's heavenly being so high up. I found this flat three years ago, quite by merest chance. I happened to be staying at the Plaza Athenée, just down the road—

ELYOT [*enthusiastically*]: Such a nice hotel, with the most enchanting courtyard with a fountain that goes plopplopplop-plopplopplopplopplop—

VICTOR: This is ridiculous, Amanda.

ELYOT [*continuing*]: Plop Plop plop plop plop plop plop plop plop plop—

AMANDA [*overriding him*]: Now, Victor, I refuse to discuss anything in the least important until after breakfast. I couldn't concentrate now, I know I couldn't.

ELYOT [*sarcastically*]: What manner. What poise. How I envy it. To be able to carry off the most embarrassing situation with such tact, and delicacy, and above all – such subtlety. Go on Amanda, you're making everything so much easier. We shall all be playing Hunt the Slipper in a minute.

AMANDA: Please don't address me, I don't wish to speak to you.

ELYOT: Splendid.

AMANDA: And what's more, I never shall again as long as I live.

ELYOT: I shall endeavour to rise above it.

AMANDA: I've been brought up to believe that it's beyond the pale, for a man to strike a woman.

ELYOT: A very poor tradition. Certain women should be struck regularly, like gongs.

AMANDA: You're an unmitigated cad, and a bully.

ELYOT: And you're an ill-mannered, bad-tempered slattern.

AMANDA [*loudly*]: Slattern indeed.

ELYOT: Yes, slattern, slattern, slattern, and fishwife.

VICTOR: Keep your mouth shut, you swine.

ELYOT: Mind your own damned business.

[*They are about to fight, when* SIBYL *rushes between them.*]

SIBYL: Stop, stop, it's no use going on like this. Stop, please. [*To* AMANDA] Help me, do, do, do, help me—

AMANDA: I'm not going to interfere. Let them fight if they want to, it will probably clear the air anyhow.

SIBYL: Yes, but—

AMANDA: Come into my room; perhaps you'd like to wash or something.

SIBYL: No, but—

AMANDA [*firmly*]: Come along.

SIBYL: Very well.

[*She tosses her head at* ELYOT, *and* AMANDA *drags her off.*]

VICTOR [*belligerently*]: Now then!

ELYOT: Now then what?

VICTOR: Are you going to take back those things you said to Amanda?

ELYOT: Certainly. I'll take back anything, if only you'll stop bellowing at me.

VICTOR [*contemptuously*]: You're a coward too.

ELYOT: They want us to fight, don't you see?

VICTOR: No, I don't. Why should they?

ELYOT: Primitive feminine instincts – warring males – very enjoyable.

VICTOR: You think you're very clever, don't you?

ELYOT: I think I'm a bit cleverer than you, but apparently that's not saying much.

VICTOR [*violently*]: What?

ELYOT: Oh, do sit down.

VICTOR: I will not.

ELYOT: Well, if you'll excuse me I will. I'm extremely tired.

[*He sits down.*]

VICTOR: Oh, for God's sake, behave like a man.

ELYOT [*patiently*]: Listen a minute, all this belligerency is very right and proper and highly traditional, but if only you'll think for a moment, you'll see that it won't get us very far.

VICTOR: To hell with all that.

ELYOT: I should like to explain that if you hit me, I shall certainly hit you, probably equally hard, if not harder. I'm just as strong as you, I should imagine. Then you'd hit me again, and I'd hit you again, and we'd go on until one or the other was knocked out. Now if you'll explain to me satisfactorily how all that can possibly improve the situation, I'll tear off my coat, and we'll go at one another hammer and tongs, immediately.

VICTOR: It would ease my mind.

ELYOT: Only if you won.

VICTOR: I should win all right.

ELYOT: Want to try?

VICTOR: Yes.

ELYOT [*jumping up*]: Here goes then— [*He tears off his coat.*]

VICTOR: Just a moment.

ELYOT: Well?

VICTOR: What did you mean about them wanting us to fight?

ELYOT: It would be balm to their vanity.

VICTOR: Do you love Amanda?

ELYOT: Is this a battle or a discussion? If it's the latter I shall put on my coat again; I don't want to catch a chill.

VICTOR: Answer my question, please.

ELYOT: Have a cigarette?

VICTOR [*stormily*]: Answer my question.

ELYOT: If you analyse it, it's rather a silly question.

VICTOR: Do you love Amanda?

ELYOT [*confidentially*]: Not very much this morning to be perfectly frank, I'd like to wring her neck. Do you love her?

VICTOR: That's beside the point.

ELYOT: On the contrary, it's the crux of the whole affair. If you do love her still, you can forgive her, and live with her in peace and harmony until you're ninety-eight.

99

VICTOR: You're apparently even more of a cad than I thought you were.

ELYOT: You are completely in the right over the whole business, don't imagine I'm not perfectly conscious of that.

VICTOR: I'm glad.

ELYOT: It's all very unfortunate.

VICTOR: Unfortunate? My God!

ELYOT: It might have been worse.

VICTOR: I'm glad you think so.

ELYOT: I do wish you'd stop about being so glad about everything.

VICTOR: What do you intend to do? That's what I want to know. What do you intend to do?

ELYOT [*suddenly serious*]: I don't know. I don't care.

VICTOR: I suppose you realise that you've broken that poor little woman's heart?

ELYOT: Which poor little woman?

VICTOR: Sibyl, of course.

ELYOT: Oh, come now, not as bad as that. She'll get over it, and forget all about me.

VICTOR: I sincerely hope so . . . for her sake.

ELYOT: Amanda will forget all about me too. Everybody will forget all about me. I might just as well lie down and die in fearful pain and suffering; nobody would care.

VICTOR: Don't talk such rot.

ELYOT: You must forgive me for taking rather a gloomy view of everything but the fact is, I suddenly feel slightly depressed.

VICTOR: I intend to divorce Amanda, naming you as co-respondent.

ELYOT: Very well.

VICTOR: And Sibyl will divorce you for Amanda. It would be foolish of either of you to attempt any defence.

ELYOT: Quite.

VICTOR: And the sooner you marry Amanda again, the better.

ELYOT: I'm not going to marry Amanda.

VICTOR: What?

ELYOT: She's a vile-tempered, wicked woman.

VICTOR: You should have thought of that before.

ELYOT: I did think of it before.

VICTOR [*firmly*]: You've got to marry her.

ELYOT: I'd rather marry a ravening leopard.

VICTOR [*angrily*]: Now look here. I'm sick of all this shilly-shallying. You're getting off a good deal more lightly than you deserve; you can consider yourself damned lucky I didn't shoot you.

ELYOT [*with sudden vehemence*]: Well, if you'd had a spark of manliness in you, you would have shot me. You're all fuss and fume, one of these cotton-wool Englishmen. I despise you.

VICTOR [*through clenched teeth*]: You despise me?

ELYOT: Yes, utterly. You're nothing but a rampaging gasbag!
[*He goes off into his room and slams the door, leaving* VICTOR *speechless with fury.* AMANDA *and* SIBYL *re-enter.*]

AMANDA [*brightly*]: Well, what's happened?

VICTOR [*sullenly*]: Nothing's happened.

AMANDA: You ought to be ashamed to admit it.

SIBYL: Where's Elyot?

VICTOR: In there.

AMANDA: What's he doing?

VICTOR [*turning angrily away*]: How do I know what he's doing?

AMANDA: If you were half the man I thought you were, he'd be bandaging himself.

SIBYL [*with defiance*]: Elyot's just as strong as Victor.

AMANDA [*savagely*]: I should like it proved.

SIBYL: There's no need to be so vindictive.

AMANDA: You were abusing Elyot like a pick-pocket to me a little while ago, now you are standing up for him.

SIBYL: I'm beginning to suspect that he wasn't quite so much to blame as I thought.

AMANDA: Oh, really?

SIBYL: You certainly have a very unpleasant temper.

AMANDA: It's a little difficult to keep up with your rapid changes of front, but you're young and inexperienced, so I forgive you freely.

SIBYL [*heatedly*]: Seeing the depths of degradation to which age and experience have brought you, I'm glad I'm as I am!

AMANDA [*with great grandeur*]: That was exceedingly rude. I think you'd better go away somewhere. [*She waves her hand vaguely.*]

SIBYL: After all, Elyot is my husband.

AMANDA: Take him with you, by all means.

SIBYL: If you're not very careful, I will! [*She goes over to* ELYOT'S *door and bangs on it.*] Elyot – Elyot—

ELYOT [*inside*]: What is it?

SIBYL: Let me in. Please, please let me in; I want to speak to you!

AMANDA: Heaven preserve me from nice women!

SIBYL: Your own reputation ought to do that.

AMANDA [*irritably*]: Oh, go to Hell!

[ELYOT *opens the door, and* SIBYL *disappears inside.* AMANDA *looks at* VICTOR, *who is standing with his back turned, staring out of the window, then she wanders about the room, making rather inadequate little attempts to tidy up. She glances at* VICTOR *again.*]

AMANDA: Victor.

VICTOR [*without turning*]: What?

AMANDA [*sadly*]: Nothing.

[*She begins to wrestle with one of the sofas in an effort to get it in place.* VICTOR *turns, sees her, and comes down and helps her, in silence.*]

VICTOR: Where does it go?

AMANDA: Over there. [*After they have placed it,* AMANDA *sits on the edge of it and gasps a little.*] Thank you, Victor.

VICTOR: Don't mention it.

AMANDA [*after a pause*]: What did you say to Elyot?

VICTOR: I told him he was beneath contempt.

AMANDA: Good.

VICTOR: I think you must be mad, Amanda.

AMANDA: I've often thought that myself.

VICTOR: I feel completely lost, completely bewildered.

AMANDA: I don't blame you. I don't feel any too cosy.

VICTOR: Had you been drinking last night?

AMANDA: Certainly not!

VICTOR: Had Elyot been drinking?

AMANDA: Yes – gallons.

VICTOR: Used he to drink before? When you were married to him?

AMANDA: Yes, terribly. Night after night he'd come home roaring and hiccoughing.

VICTOR: Disgusting!

AMANDA: Yes, wasn't it?

VICTOR: Did he really strike you last night?

AMANDA: Repeatedly. I'm bruised beyond recognition.

VICTOR [*suspecting slight exaggeration*]: Amanda!

AMANDA [*putting her hand on his arm*]: O Victor, I'm most awfully sorry to have given you so much trouble, really I am! I've behaved badly, I know, but something strange happened to me. I can't explain it, there's no excuse, but I am ashamed of having made you unhappy.

VICTOR: I can't understand it at all. I've tried to, but I can't. It all seems so unlike you.

AMANDA: It isn't really unlike me, that's the trouble. I ought never to have married you; I'm a bad lot.

VICTOR: Amanda!

AMANDA: Don't contradict me. I know I'm a bad lot.

VICTOR: I wasn't going to contradict you.

AMANDA: Victor!

VICTOR: You appal me – absolutely!

AMANDA: Go on, go on, I deserve it.

VICTOR: I didn't come here to accuse you; there's no sense in that!

AMANDA: Why did you come?

VICTOR: To find out what you want me to do.

AMANDA: Divorce me, I suppose, as soon as possible. I won't make any difficulties. I'll go away, far away, Morocco, or Tunis, or somewhere. I shall probably catch some dreadful disease, and die out there, all alone – oh dear!

VICTOR: It's no use pitying yourself.

AMANDA: I seem to be the only one who does. I might just as well enjoy it. [*She sniffs.*] I'm thoroughly unprincipled; Sibyl was right!

VICTOR [*irritably*]: Sibyl's an ass.

AMANDA [*brightening slightly*]: Yes, she is rather, isn't she? I can't think why Elyot ever married her.

VICTOR: Do you love him?

AMANDA: She seems so insipid, somehow—

VICTOR: Do you love him?

AMANDA: Of course, she's very pretty, I suppose, in rather a shallow way, but still—

VICTOR: Amanda!

AMANDA: Yes, Victor?

VICTOR: You haven't answered my question.

AMANDA: I've forgotten what it was.

VICTOR [*turning away*]: You're hopeless – hopeless.

AMANDA: Don't be angry; it's all much too serious to be angry about.

VICTOR: You're talking utter nonsense!

AMANDA: No, I'm not, I mean it. It's ridiculous for us all to stand round arguing with one another. You'd much better go back to England and let your lawyers deal with the whole thing.

VICTOR: But what about you?

AMANDA: I'll be all right.

VICTOR: I only want to know one thing, and you won't tell me.

AMANDA: What is it?

VICTOR: Do you love Elyot?

AMANDA: No, I hate him. When I saw him again suddenly at Deauville, it was an odd sort of shock. It swept me away completely. He attracted me; he always has attracted me, but only the worst part of me. I see that now.

VICTOR: I can't understand why? He's so terribly trivial and superficial.

AMANDA: That sort of attraction can't be explained, it's a sort of a chemical what d'you call 'em.

VICTOR: Yes; it must be!

AMANDA: I don't expect you to understand, and I'm not going to try to excuse myself in any way. Elyot was the first love affair of my life, and in spite of all the suffering he caused me before, there must have been a little spark left smouldering, which burst into flame when I came face to face with him again. I completely lost grip of myself and behaved like a fool, for which I shall pay all right, you needn't worry about that.

But perhaps one day, when all this is dead and done with, you and I might meet and be friends. That's something to hope for, anyhow. Goodbye, Victor dear. [*She holds out her hand.*]

VICTOR [*shaking her hand mechanically*]: Do you want to marry him?

AMANDA: I'd rather marry a boa constrictor.

VICTOR: I can't go away and leave you with a man who drinks, and knocks you about.

AMANDA: You needn't worry about leaving me, as though I were a sort of parcel. I can look after myself.

VICTOR: You said just now you were going away to Tunis, to die.

AMANDA: I've changed my mind. It's the wrong time of the year for Tunis. I shall go somewhere quite different. I believe Brioni is very nice in the summer.

VICTOR: Why won't you be serious for just one moment?

AMANDA: I've told you, it's no use.

VICTOR: If it will make things any easier for you, I won't divorce you.

AMANDA: Victor!

VICTOR: We can live apart until Sibyl has got her decree against Elyot, then, some time after that, I'll let you divorce me.

AMANDA [*turning away*]: I see you're determined to make me serious, whether I like it or not.

VICTOR: I married you because I loved you.

AMANDA: Stop it, Victor! Stop it! I won't listen!

VICTOR: I expect I love you still; one doesn't change all in a minute. You never loved me. I see that now, of course, so perhaps everything has turned out for the best, really.

AMANDA: I thought I loved you, honestly I did.

VICTOR: Yes, I know, that's all right.

AMANDA: What an escape you've had.

VICTOR: I've said that to myself often during the last few days.

AMANDA: There's no need to rub it in.

VICTOR: Do you agree about the divorce business?

AMANDA: Yes. It's very, very generous of you.

VICTOR: It will save you some of the mud-slinging. We might persuade Sibyl not to name you.

AMANDA [*ruefully*]: Yes, we might.

VICTOR: Perhaps she'll change her mind about divorcing him.

AMANDA: Perhaps. She certainly went into the bedroom with a predatory look in her eye.

VICTOR: Would you be pleased if that happened?

AMANDA: Delighted.

[*She laughs suddenly.* VICTOR *looks at her, curiously.* SIBYL *and* ELYOT *come out of the bedroom. There is an awkward silence for a moment.*]

SIBYL [*looking at* AMANDA *triumphantly*]: Elyot and I have come to a decision.

AMANDA: How very nice!

VICTOR: What is it?

AMANDA: Don't be silly, Victor. Look at their faces.

ELYOT: Feminine intuition, very difficult.

AMANDA [*looking at* SIBYL]: Feminine determination, very praiseworthy.

SIBYL: I am not going to divorce Elyot for a year.

AMANDA: I congratulate you.

ELYOT [*defiantly*]: Sibyl has behaved like an angel.

AMANDA: Well, it was certainly her big moment.

[LOUISE *comes staggering in with a large tray of coffee and rolls, etc.; she stands peering over the edge of it, not knowing where to put it.*]

ELYOT: Il faut le met sur la petite table là-bas.

LOUISE: Oui, monsieur.

[ELYOT *and* VICTOR *hurriedly clear the things off the side table, and* LOUISE *puts the tray down, and goes back into the kitchen.* AMANDA *and* SIBYL *eye one another.*]

AMANDA: It all seems very amicable.

SIBYL: It is, thank you.

AMANDA: I don't wish to depress you, but Victor isn't going to divorce me either.

ELYOT [*looking up sharply*]: What!

AMANDA: I believe I asked you once before this morning, never to speak to me again.

ELYOT: I only said 'What'. It was a general exclamation denoting extreme satisfaction.

AMANDA [politely to SIBYL]: Do sit down, won't you?

SIBYL: I'm afraid I must be going now. I'm catching the Golden Arrow; it leaves at twelve.

ELYOT [coaxingly]: You have time for a little coffee, surely?

SIBYL: No, I really must go!

ELYOT: I shan't be seeing you again for such a long time.

AMANDA [brightly]: Living apart? How wise!

ELYOT [ignoring her]: Please, Sibyl, do stay!

SIBYL [looking at AMANDA with a glint in her eye]: Very well, just for a little.

AMANDA: Sit down, Victor, darling.

[They all sit down in silence. AMANDA smiles sweetly at SIBYL and holds up the coffee pot and milk jug.]
Half and half?

SIBYL: Yes, please.

AMANDA [sociably]: What would one do without one's morning coffee? That's what I often ask myself.

ELYOT: Is it?

AMANDA [withering him with a look]: Victor, sugar for Sibyl. [To SIBYL] It would be absurd for me to call you anything but Sibyl, wouldn't it?

SIBYL [not to be outdone]: Of course, I shall call you Mandy.

[AMANDA represses a shudder.]

ELYOT: O God! We're off again. What weather!

[AMANDA hands SIBYL her coffee.]

SIBYL: Thank you.

VICTOR: What's the time?

ELYOT: If the clock's still going after last night, it's ten-fifteen.

AMANDA [handing VICTOR cup of coffee]: Here, Victor dear.

VICTOR: Thanks.

AMANDA: Sibyl, sugar for Victor.

ELYOT: I should like some coffee, please.

[AMANDA pours some out for him, and hands it to him in silence.]

AMANDA [to VICTOR]: Brioche?

VICTOR [jumping]: What?

AMANDA: Would you like a brioche?

VICTOR: No, thank you.

ELYOT: I would. And some butter, and some jam. [*He helps himself.*]

AMANDA [*to* SIBYL]: Have you ever been to Brioni?

SIBYL: No. It's in the Adriatic, isn't it?

VICTOR: The Baltic, I think.

SIBYL: I made sure it was in the Adriatic.

AMANDA: I had an aunt who went there once.

ELYOT [*with his mouth full*]: I once had an aunt who went to Tasmania.

> [AMANDA *looks at him stonily. He winks at her, and she looks away hurriedly.*]

VICTOR: Funny how the South of France has become so fashionable in the summer, isn't it?

SIBYL: Yes, awfully funny.

ELYOT: I've been laughing about it for months.

AMANDA: Personally, I think it's a bit too hot, although of course one can lie in the water all day.

SIBYL: Yes, the bathing is really divine!

VICTOR: A friend of mine has a house right on the edge of Cap Ferrat.

SIBYL: Really?

VICTOR: Yes, right on the edge.

AMANDA: That must be marvellous!

VICTOR: Yes, he seems to like it very much.

> [*The conversation languishes slightly.*]

AMANDA [*with great vivacity*]: Do you know, I really think I love travelling more than anything else in the world! It always gives me such a tremendous feeling of adventure. First of all, the excitement of packing, and getting your passport visa'd and everything, then the thrill of actually starting, and trundling along on trains and ships, and then the most thrilling thing of all, arriving at strange places, and seeing strange people, and eating strange foods—

ELYOT: And making strange noises afterwards.

> [AMANDA *chokes violently.* VICTOR *jumps up and tries to offer assistance, but she waves him away, and continues to choke.*]

VICTOR [*to* ELYOT]: That was a damned fool thing to do.

ELYOT: How did I know she was going to choke?

VICTOR [*to* AMANDA]: Here, drink some coffee.

AMANDA [*breathlessly gasping*]: Leave me alone. I'll be all right in a minute.

VICTOR [*to* ELYOT]: You waste too much time trying to be funny.

SIBYL [*up in arms*]: It's no use talking to Elyot like that; it wasn't his fault.

VICTOR: Of course it was his fault entirely, making rotten stupid jokes—

SIBYL: I thought what Elyot said was funny.

VICTOR: Well, all I can say is, you must have a very warped sense of humour.

SIBYL: That's better than having none at all.

VICTOR: I fail to see what humour there is in incessant trivial flippancy.

SIBYL: You couldn't be flippant if you tried until you were blue in the face.

VICTOR: I shouldn't dream of trying.

SIBYL: It must be very sad not to be able to see any fun in anything.

[AMANDA *stops choking, and looks at* ELYOT. *He winks at her again, and she smiles.*]

VICTOR: Fun! I should like you to tell me what fun there is in—

SIBYL: I pity you, I really do. I've been pitying you ever since we left Deauville.

VICTOR: I'm sure it's very nice of you, but quite unnecessary.

SIBYL: And I pity you more than ever now.

VICTOR: Why now particularly?

SIBYL: If you don't see why, I'm certainly not going to tell you.

VICTOR: I see no reason for you to try to pick a quarrel with me. I've tried my best to be pleasant to you, and comfort you.

SIBYL: You weren't very comforting when I lost my trunk.

VICTOR: I have little patience with people who go about losing luggage.

SIBYL: I don't go about losing luggage. It's the first time I've lost anything in my life.

VICTOR: I find that hard to believe.

SIBYL: Anyhow, if you'd tipped the porter enough, everything would have been all right. Small economies never pay; it's absolutely no use—

VICTOR: Oh, for God's sake be quiet!

[AMANDA *lifts her hand as though she were going to interfere, but* ELYOT *grabs her wrist. They look at each other for a moment; she lets her hand rest in his.*]

SIBYL [*rising from the table*]: How dare you speak to me like that!

VICTOR [*also rising*]: Because you've been irritating me for days.

SIBYL [*outraged*]: Oh!

VICTOR [*coming down to her*]: You're one of the most completely idiotic women I've ever met.

SIBYL: And you're certainly the rudest man I've ever met!

VICTOR: Well then, we're quits, aren't we?

SIBYL [*shrilly*]: One thing, you'll get your deserts all right.

VICTOR: What do you mean by that?

SIBYL: You know perfectly well what I mean. And it'll serve you right for being weak-minded enough to allow that woman to get round you so easily.

VICTOR: What about you? Letting that unprincipled roué persuade you to take him back again!

[AMANDA *and* ELYOT *are laughing silently.* ELYOT *blows her a lingering kiss across the table.*]

SIBYL: He's nothing of the sort, he's just been victimised, as you were victimised.

VICTOR: Victimised! What damned nonsense!

SIBYL [*furiously*]: It isn't damned nonsense! You're very fond of swearing and blustering and threatening, but when it comes to the point you're as weak as water. Why, a blind cat could see what you've let yourself in for.

VICTOR [*equally furious*]: Stop making those insinuations.

SIBYL: I'm not insinuating anything. When I think of all the things you said about her, it makes me laugh, it does really; to see how completely she's got you again.

VICTOR: You can obviously speak with great authority, having had the intelligence to marry a drunkard.

SIBYL: So that's what she's been telling you. I might have known it! I suppose she said he struck her too!

VICTOR: Yes, she did, and I'm quite sure it's perfectly true.

SIBYL: I expect she omitted to tell you that she drank fourteen glasses of brandy last night straight off; and that the reason their first marriage was broken up was that she used to come home at all hours of the night, screaming and hiccoughing.

VICTOR: If he told you that, he's a filthy liar.

SIBYL: He isn't – he isn't!

VICTOR: And if you believe it, you're a silly scatter-brained little fool.

SIBYL [*screaming*]: How dare you speak to me like that! How dare you! I've never been so insulted in my life! How dare you!

[AMANDA *and* ELYOT *rise quietly, and go, hand in hand, towards the front door.*]

VICTOR [*completely giving way*]: It's a tremendous relief to me to have an excuse to insult you. I've had to listen to your weeping and wailings for days. You've clacked at me, and snivelled at me until you've nearly driven me insane, and I controlled my nerves and continued to try to help you and look after you, because I was sorry for you. I always thought you were stupid from the first, but I must say I never realised that you were a malicious little vixen as well!

SIBYL [*shrieking*]: Stop it! Stop it! You insufferable great brute!

[*She slaps his face hard, and he takes her by the shoulders and shakes her like a rat, as* AMANDA *and* ELYOT *go smilingly out of the door, with their suitcases, and—*]

THE CURTAIN FALLS

Curiously, the words of the song which Amanda sings in Act I and the lovers sing together in Act II are not part of the published text of Private Lives. *Many of us probably heard them first on an HMV record of two excerpts from the play which Noël and Gertie recorded in 1930. They are still to be heard on a compact disc today but, in case that is out of reach, here they are.*

III

Some Day I'll Find You

When one is lonely the days are long;
You seem so near
But never appear.
Each night I sing you a lover's song;
Please try to hear,
My dear, my dear.

Verse 2

Can't you remember the fun we had?
Time is so fleet,
Why shouldn't we meet?
When you're away from me days are sad;
Life's not complete,
My sweet, my sweet.

Refrain

Some day I'll find you,
Moonlight behind you,
True to the dream I am dreaming
As I draw near you
You'll smile a little smile;
For a little while
We shall stand
Hand in hand.
I'll leave you never,
Love you for ever,
All our past sorrow redeeming,
Try to make it true,
Say you love me too.
Some day I'll find you again.

During the London run of *Private Lives*, I discussed with Cochran the idea of doing a big spectacular production at the Coliseum. I felt an urge to test my producing powers on a large scale. My mind's eye visualised a series of tremendous mob scenes – the storming of the Bastille – the massacre of the Huguenots – I believe even the Decline and Fall of the Roman Empire flirted with me for a little.

I continued the search, until one day I happened to buy, at Foyle's in the Charing Cross Road, some ancient bound volumes of *Black and White* and the *Illustrated London News*. This was chance, and extremely happy chance. In the first volume I opened there was a full-page picture of a troop-ship leaving for the Boer War, and the moment I saw it I knew that I had found what I wanted. I can't explain why it rang the bell so sharply, I only know that it did. The tunes came into my mind first, tunes belonging to my very earliest childhood; 'Dolly Gray', 'The Absent-minded Beggar', 'Soldiers of the Queen', 'Bluebell' (later this, but I neither knew nor cared). I played them on the piano immediately. G. B. Stern, who was coming to tea, found me in a state of high excitement; by then I had progressed, musically, quite a long way through the years; I'm not sure, but I think she entered to the tune of 'Tipperary'.

The emotional basis of *Cavalcade* was undoubtedly music. The whole story was threaded on to a string of popular melodies. This ultimately was a big contributing factor to its success. Popular tunes probe the memory more swiftly than anything else, and *Cavalcade*, whatever else it did, certainly awakened many echoes.

My original story was different from what finally emerged, but the shape was the same, New Year's Eve 1899 to New Year's Eve 1930. Events took precedence first in my mind, and against them I moved a group of people – the bright young people of the nineties, the play was to finish with their children – the same eager emptiness, but a different jargon. After a while, I realised that the play should be bigger than that. I had flogged the bright young people enough, my vehemence against them had congealed, they were now no more than damp squibs, my Poor Little Rich Girls and Dance, Little Ladies. Thirty years of English life seen through their eyes would be uninspired, to say the least of it. Presently my real characters appeared in two classes: 'the Marryots', and 'Ellen' and 'Bridges'.

'Jane Marryot' took shape in my mind quite early. She seemed real to me and still does, a bit of my own mother and millions of others, too; ordinary, kind, and unobtrusively brave; capable of deep suffering and incapable of cheap complaint. I was proud of 'Jane Marryot' from the first.

When Cavalcade was eventually staged it was at the Theatre Royal, Drury Lane and not the Coliseum, but Coward's original ambition remained intact: a pageant of British history in the first third of the century seen through the experience of two families. It appeared at a time when national confidence was low, and one reason for its success must have been the emphasis on our capacity for private and public courage. Since 1930 there have not been many opportunities to see Cavalcade but even on the page there are scenes which prove, without question, Coward's ability to distil a great event or emotion into a tiny space.

CAVALCADE

Part Two:

SCENE 5

Principals: EDWARD, EDITH.

SCENE: *The deck of an Atlantic liner. This is quite a small inset scene. The rail of the Promenade Deck faces the audience. Behind it can be seen the lighted windows of the lounge. Above can be seen vaguely the Boat Deck, with ventilators and a funnel silhouetted against the stars.*
TIME: *About 7 p.m. Sunday, 14 April 1912.*

EDWARD *and* EDITH, *he in dinner-jacket, she in evening dress, are leaning on the rail.*

EDITH: It's too big, the Atlantic, isn't it?
EDWARD: Far too big.
EDITH: And too deep.
EDWARD: Much, much too deep.
EDITH: I don't care a bit, do you?
EDWARD: Not a scrap.
EDITH: Wouldn't it be awful if a magician came to us and said: 'Unless you count accurately every single fish in the Atlantic you die tonight?'
EDWARD: We should die tonight.
EDITH: How much would you mind – dying, I mean?
EDWARD: I don't know really – a good deal, I expect.
EDITH: I don't believe I should mind so very much now. You see, we could never in our whole lives be happier than we are now, could we?
EDWARD: Darling, there *are* different sorts of happiness.
EDITH: This is the best sort.
EDWARD [*kissing her*]: Sweetheart!

EDITH: Don't, darling, we don't want any more of the stewards to know we're on our honeymoon.

EDWARD: Why not? It gives them so much vicarious pleasure. Most of them have forgotten what it was like.

EDITH: Are all honeymoons like this?

EDWARD [*firmly*]: Exactly.

EDITH: O Edward – that's rather disheartening, isn't it? I do so want this to be unique.

EDWARD: It is, for us.

EDITH: Did you ever think when we were children, going to the pantomime, and going to the Zoo, and playing soldiers, that we should ever be married?

EDWARD: Of course I didn't.

EDITH: Was I nice as a child?

EDWARD: Horrible!

EDITH: So were you, and so was Joe – vile. You always used to take sides against me.

EDWARD: And yet we all liked one another really.

EDITH: I think I liked Joe better than you, but then he was younger and easier to manage. Dear Joe, he was awfully funny at the wedding, wasn't he?

EDWARD: Ribald little beast!

EDITH: He has no reverence, I'm afraid.

EDWARD: Absolutely none.

EDITH: He's passing gallantly through the chorus-girl phase now, isn't he?

EDWARD: Gallantly but not quickly.

EDITH: Well, darling, you took your time over it.

EDWARD: Now then, Edith—

EDITH: You had several affairs before you married me, didn't you?

EDWARD: Light of my life, shut up!

EDITH: You'd be awfully cross if *I* had, wouldn't you?

EDWARD: Had what?

EDITH: Affairs – love affairs – before you.

EDWARD: Did you?

EDITH: Hundreds.

EDWARD: Liar!

EDITH: I rather wish I had, really. Perhaps I should have learnt some tricks to hold you with when you begin to get tired of me.

EDWARD: I never shall, tricks or no tricks.

EDITH: Yes, you will one day. You're bound to; people always do. This complete loveliness that we feel together now will fade, so many years and the gilt wears off the gingerbread, and just the same as the stewards, we shall have forgotten what it was like.

EDWARD [*seriously*]: Answer me one thing, truly, dearest. Have you ever seen gingerbread with gilt on it?

EDITH: Never!

EDWARD: Then the whole argument is disposed of. Anyhow, look at father and mother; they're perfectly happy and devoted, and they always have been.

EDITH: They had a better chance at the beginning. Things weren't changing so swiftly; life wasn't so restless.

EDWARD: How long do you give us?

EDITH: I don't know – and Edward – [*She turns to him*] I don't care. This is our moment – complete and heavenly. I'm not afraid of anything. This is our own, for ever.

[EDWARD *takes* EDITH *in his arms and kisses her.*]

EDWARD: Do you think a nice warming glass of sherry would make it any more heavenly?

EDITH: You have no soul, darling, but I'm very attached to you. Come on—

[EDITH *takes up her cloak which has been hanging over the rail, and they walk away. The cloak has been covering a lifebelt, and when it is withdrawn the words S.S.* Titanic *can be seen in black letters on the white.*

The lights fade into complete darkness, but the letters remain glowing as the orchestra plays very softly and tragically 'Nearer My God to Thee'.]

The doomed honeymoon couple are the Marryots' older son and his childhood sweetheart. Edward's young brother, Joe, joins up on the out-break of war in 1914. Jane Marryot's famous toast, which is spoken on

New Year's Eve 1929, embraces the fact of Joe's death in action, just before the Armistice. Cavalcade ends with a song that fixes firmly the moment when the Jazz Age ended and the Depression began.

Part Three

SCENE 1 (EXCERPT)

Principals: ROBERT and JANE MARRYOT.

SCENE: *Drawing-room of their London house.*

JANE: Well, Robert – here we go again.

ROBERT: I believe you laugh at me inside – for my annual sentimental outburst.

JANE: No dear, I don't laugh at you.

ROBERT: One more year behind us.

JANE: One more year before us.

ROBERT: Do you mind?

JANE: Oh, no – everything passes – even time.

ROBERT: It seems incredible, doesn't it? Here we are in this same room!

JANE: Yes. I've hated it for years.

ROBERT: Do you want to move?

JANE: Of course not.

ROBERT: We might have some new curtains.

JANE: We have, dear.

ROBERT: Good God, so we have! I never noticed.

JANE: They've only been up a week.

ROBERT: They look very nice.

JANE: Dear Robert. [*She pats* ROBERT'S *hand.*] What toast have you in mind for tonight – something gay and original, I hope?

ROBERT: Just our old friend – the future. The Future of England.

JANE: It's starting – the champagne, quick!

[ROBERT *gets a champagne bottle out of the bucket and struggles with it.* JANE *opens the window.*]

ROBERT: I can't get the damned thing open.

JANE: Let me try.

ROBERT [doing it]:   There!

> [JANE holds the glasses.
>
> ROBERT fills the glasses.
>
> Meanwhile the chimes and sirens are beginning outside.]

JANE [holding up her glass]:   First of all, my dear, I drink to you. Loyal and loving always. [She drinks.] Now, then, let's couple the future of England with the past of England. The glories and victories and triumphs that are over, and the sorrows that are over, too. Let's drink to our sons who made part of the pattern and to our hearts that died with them. Let's drink to the spirit of gallantry and courage that made a strange Heaven out of unbelievable Hell, and let's drink to the hope that one day this country of ours, which we love so much, will find dignity and greatness and peace again.

> [They both lift their glasses and drink as the lights fade.]

SCENE 2

Principals: ROBERT, JANE, FANNY, MARGARET, ELLEN, FULL COMPANY.

SCENE: A Night-club.

TIME: Evening – 1930.

This Scene begins with a night-club in which FANNY is singing, seated on a piano. The decoration is angular and strange, and the song she is singing is oddly discordant.

Twentieth-Century Blues

Verse

Why is it that civilised humanity
Must make the world so wrong?
In this hurly burly of insanity

Your dreams cannot last long.
We've reached a deadline
The Press headline – every sorrow,
Blues value is News value tomorrow.

Refrain

Blues, Twentieth-Century Blues, are getting me down.
Who's escaped those weary Twentieth-Century Blues.
Why, if there's a God in the sky, why shouldn't he grin?
High above this dreary Twentieth-Century din,
In this strange illusion,
Chaos and confusion,
People seem to lose their way.
What is there to strive for,
Love or keep alive for? Say—
Hey, hey, call it a day.
Blues, nothing to win or to lose.
It's getting me down.
Blues, I've got those weary Twentieth-Century Blues.

[*When the song is finished, people rise from table and dance without apparently any particular enjoyment; it is the dull dancing of habit. The lights fade away from everything but the dancers, who appear to be rising in the air. They disappear and down stage Left, six 'incurables' in blue hospital uniform are sitting making baskets. They disappear and* FANNY *is seen singing her song for a moment, then far away up stage a jazz band is seen playing wildly. Then down stage* JANE *and* ROBERT *standing with glasses of champagne held aloft, then* ELLEN *sitting in front of a radio loudspeaker; then* MARGARET *dancing with a young man. The visions are repeated quicker and quicker, while across the darkness runs a Riley light sign spelling out news. Noise grows louder and louder. Steam rivets, loudspeakers, jazz bands, aeroplane propellers, etc., until the general effect is complete chaos.*

Suddenly it all fades into darkness and silence and away at the back a Union Jack glows through the blackness.

The lights slowly come up and the whole stage is composed of massive tiers, upon which stand the entire company. The Union Jack flies over their heads as they sing 'God Save the King'.]

THE END

After playing Private Lives *in both London and New York, and writing and directing* Cavalcade, *most ordinary mortals might have thought that they deserved a holiday while waiting for the Lunts to become available to appear in* Design for Living. *Not, however, Noël Coward. He filled the gap in his professional life by undertaking another revue for C. B. Cochran. This time all the material was his own, he directed the complete show and, on one particularly hectic occasion, even conducted the orchestra.*

This revue, after various titles had been suggested and discarded, was ultimately called *Words and Music* and was presented by C. B. Cochran at the Opera House, Manchester on 25 August 1932. On 16 September it opened at the Adelphi in London where it ran for several months, not, as I had hoped, for two years. It was a good revue on the whole and received excellent notices but what it lacked was a big star, or better still, two big stars. The cast included Ivy St Helier, Joyce Barbour, John Mills, Romney Brent and Doris Hare, all of whom were expert performers but none of whom at this time had that indisputable star quality which commands queues at the box-office. Later it was produced in New York under the title *Set to Music* with Beatrice Lillie and Richard Haydn. Nobody could question the 'star' status of Beatrice Lillie but even with her name over the marquee the show, after three months' capacity business, lingered on for a further month or so and then closed. All of which, I am reluctantly forced to admit, proves that the revue itself wasn't quite as good as it should have been.

When I was a very little boy my beloved housemaid-cum-nurse, Emma, used to admonish me by saying, 'Don't be too sharp or you'll cut yourself!' This I think, on looking back, was what was wrong with *Words and Music*. It was too clever by half. It contained too much satire and too little glamour to attract the masses. However, as it didn't exactly flop humiliatingly in either London or New York, I can quite happily chalk it up as a near miss and remember it with affection.

'Mad About the Boy' is usually heard nowadays as a torch song, a decorous equivalent to Rodgers and Hart's 'Bewitched'. In spite of its wonderful, langorous melody it was originally a much more elaborate and satirical number for four different women.

Mad About the Boy

Verse

SOCIETY   I met him at a party just a couple of years ago,
WOMAN: He was rather over-hearty and ridiculous,
          But as I'd seen him on the Screen
          He cast a certain spell.
          I basked in his attraction for a couple of hours or so,
          His manners were a fraction too meticulous,
          If he was real or not I couldn't tell
              But like a silly fool, I fell.

Refrain

Mad about the boy,
I know it's stupid to be mad about the boy,
I'm so ashamed of it
But must admit
The sleepless nights I've had about the boy.
On the Silver Screen
He melts my foolish heart in every single scene.
Although I'm quite aware
That here and there
Are traces of the cad about the boy,

Lord knows I'm not a fool girl,
I really shouldn't care,
Lord knows I'm not a schoolgirl
In the flurry of her first affair.
Will it ever cloy?
This odd diversity of misery and joy,
I'm feeling quite insane
And young again
And all because I'm mad about the boy.

Refrain 2

SCHOOL- Mad about the boy,
GIRL: It's simply scrumptious to be mad about the boy,
        I know that quite sincerely
        Housman really
        Wrote *The Shropshire Lad* about the boy.
        In my English Prose
        I've done a tracing of his forehead and his nose
        And there is, honour bright,
        A certain slight
        Effect of Galahad about the boy.
        I've talked to Rosie Hooper,
        She feels the same as me,
        She says that Gary Cooper
        Doesn't thrill her to the same degree.
        In *Can Love Destroy?*
        When he meets Garbo in a suit of corduroy,
        He gives a little frown
        And knocks her down.
        Oh dear, oh dear, I'm mad about the boy.

Refrain 3

COCKNEY: Mad about the boy,
        I know I'm potty but I'm mad about the boy.
        He sets me 'eart on fire
        With love's desire,
        In fact I've got it bad about the boy.
        When I do the rooms

I see 'is face in all the brushes and the brooms.
Last week I strained me back
And got the sack
And 'ad a row with Dad about the boy.
I'm finished with Navarro,
I'm tired of Richard Dix,
I'm pierced by Cupid's arrow
Every Wednesday from four till six.
'Ow I should enjoy
To let 'im treat me like a plaything or a toy,
I'd give my all to him
And crawl to him,
So 'elp me Gawd I'm mad about the boy.

Verse 2

TART: It seems a little silly
For a girl of my age and weight
To walk down Piccadilly
In a haze of love.
It ought to take a good deal more to get a bad girl down,
I should have been exempt, for
My particular kind of Fate
Has taught me such contempt for
Every phase of love,
And now I've been and spent my last half-crown
To weep about a painted clown.

Refrain 4

Mad about the boy,
It's pretty funny but I'm mad about the boy,
He has a gay appeal
That makes me feel
There's maybe something sad about the boy.
Walking down the street,
His eyes look out at me from people that I meet,
I can't believe it's true
But when I'm blue
In some strange way I'm glad about the boy.

I'm hardly sentimental,
Love isn't so sublime,
I have to pay my rental
And I can't afford to waste much time,
If I could employ
A little magic that would finally destroy
This dream that pains me
And enchains me,
But I can't because I'm mad about the boy.

In his memoir My Life With Noël Coward, *Graham Payn reprinted a last, lost refrain for this song. It was written for the 1938 New York version of the revue. A dapper businessman in formal black coat and striped trousers is discovered in a smart office setting:*

Mad about the boy,
I know it's silly but I'm mad about the boy,
And even Doctor Freud
Cannot explain
Those vexing dreams I've had about the boy.
When I told my wife,
She said: 'I've never heard such nonsense in my life!'
Her lack of sympathy
Embarrassed me
And made me frankly *glad* about the boy.
My doctor can't advise me,
He'd help me if he could;
Three times he's tried to psychoanalyse me
But it's just no good.
People I employ
Have the impertinence to call me Myrna Loy.
I rise above it,
Frankly love it,
'Cos I'm absolutely mad about the boy!

To nobody's great surprise this chorus was not heard in the show . . . This revue, both in London and New York, provided a home for those 'Mad Dogs and Englishmen', originally composed in Vietnam at the start of the decade.

In *Words and Music* Romney Brent sang it ['Mad Dogs'] as a missionary in one of Britain's tropical colonies. Since then I have sung it myself *ad nauseam*. On one occasion it achieved international significance. This was a dinner party given by Mr Winston Churchill on board H M S *Prince of Wales* in honour of President Roosevelt on the evening following the signing of the Atlantic Charter. From an eye-witness description of the scene it appears that the two world leaders became involved in a heated argument as to whether 'In Bangkok at twelve o'clock they foam at the mouth and run' came at the end of the first refrain or at the end of the second. President Roosevelt held firmly to the latter view and refused to budge even under the impact of Churchillian rhetoric. In this he was right and when, a little while later, I asked Mr Churchill about the incident, he admitted defeat like a man.

(The Noël Coward Song Book, 1953)

There were some other additions for the New York version of the show, one of which gives an imperishable picture of Thirties Society at play.

During the summer of 1937 or 1938, I forget which, Elsa Maxwell gave a party in the South of France. It was a 'Beach Party' and when she invited Grace Moore, Beatrice Lillie and me she explained that we were to 'come as we were' and that it would be 'just ourselves'. When we arrived ('as we were') we discovered that 'just ourselves' meant about a hundred of us, all in the last stages of evening dress . . . This whole glittering episode was my original inspiration for 'I Went to a Marvellous Party'.

(The Noël Coward Song Book, 1953)

It was delivered, appropriately enough, by Beatrice Lillie.

I've Been to a Marvellous Party

Verse 1

Quite for no reason
I'm here for the Season
And high as a kite,
Living in error
With Maud at Cap Ferrat
Which couldn't be right.
Everyone's here and frightfully gay,
Nobody cares what people say,
Though the Riviera
Seems really much queerer
Than Rome at its height,
Yesterday night—

Refrain 1

I've been to a marvellous party
With Nounou and Nada and Nell,
It was in the fresh air
And we went as we were
And we stayed as we were
Which was Hell.
Poor Grace started singing at midnight
And didn't stop singing till four;
We knew the excitement was bound to begin
When Laura got blind on Dubonnet and gin
And scratched her veneer with a Cartier pin,
I couldn't have liked it more.

Refrain 2

I've been to a marvellous party,
I must say the fun was intense,
We all had to do
What the people we knew
Would be doing a hundred years hence.
Dear Cecil arrived wearing armour,

Some shells and a black feather boa,
Poor Millicent wore a surrealist comb
Made of bits of mosaic from St Peter's in Rome,
But the weight was so great that she had to go home,
I couldn't have liked it more!

Verse 2

People's behaviour
Away from Belgravia
Would make you aghast,
So much variety
Watching Society
Scampering past,
If you have any mind at all
Gibbon's divine *Decline and Fall*
Seems pretty flimsy,
No more than a whimsy,
By way of contrast
On Saturday last—

Refrain 3

I've been to a marvellous party,
We didn't start dinner till ten
And young Bobbie Carr
Did a stunt at the bar
With a lot of extraordinary men;
Dear Baba arrived with a turtle
Which shattered us all to the core,
The Grand Duke was dancing a foxtrot with me
When suddenly Cyril screamed Fiddledidee
And ripped off his trousers and jumped in the sea,
I couldn't have liked it more.

Refrain 4

I've been to a marvellous party,
Elise made an entrance with May,
You'd never have guessed
From her fisherman's vest

That her bust had been whittled away.
Poor Lulu got fried on Chianti
And talked about esprit de corps.
Maurice made a couple of passes at Gus
And Freddie, who hates any kind of a fuss,
Did half the Big Apple and twisted his truss,
I couldn't have liked it more.

Refrain 5

I've been to a marvellous party,
We played the most wonderful game,
Maureen disappeared
And came back in a beard
And we all had to guess at her name!
We talked about growing old gracefully
And Elsie who's seventy-four
Said, 'A, it's a question of being sincere,
And B, if you're supple you've nothing to fear.'
Then she swung upside down from a glass chandelier,
I couldn't have liked it more.

Nearly all of Coward's songs were written for particular plays, musicals or revues. One of them – and one of the most brilliantly successful – was not.

Its universal appeal lies, I believe, in its passionate sincerity. It is a genuine *cri de coeur* and as such cannot fail to ring true. Unhappily, its effectiveness, from the point of view of propaganda, has been negligible. I had hoped, by writing it, to discourage misguided maternal ambition, to deter those dreadful eager mothers from making beasts of themselves, boring the hell out of me and wasting their own and my time, but I have not succeeded . . . This is saddening, of course, but realising that the road of the social reformer is paved with disillusion I have determined to rise above it.

(*The Noël Coward Song Book*, 1953)

Mrs Worthington

Regarding yours, dear Mrs Worthington,
Of Wednesday the 23rd,
Although your baby
May be
Keen on a stage career,
How can I make it clear
That this is not a good idea.
For her to hope,
Dear Mrs Worthington,
Is on the face of it absurd,
Her personality
Is not in reality
Inviting enough,
Exciting enough
For this particular sphere.

Refrain 1

Don't put your daughter on the stage, Mrs Worthington,
Don't put your daughter on the stage,
The profession is overcrowded
And the struggle's pretty tough
And admitting the fact
She's burning to act,
That isn't quite enough.
She has nice hands, to give the wretched girl her due,
But don't you think her bust is too
Developed for her age,
I repeat,
Mrs Worthington,
Sweet,
Mrs Worthington,
Don't put your daughter on the stage.

Refrain 2

Don't put your daughter on the stage, Mrs Worthington,

Don't put your daughter on the stage,
She's a bit of an ugly duckling
You must honestly confess,
And the width of her seat
Would surely defeat
Her chances of success,
It's a loud voice, and though it's not exactly flat,
She'll need a little more than that
To earn a living wage.
On my knees,
Mrs Worthington,
Please,
Mrs Worthington,
Don't put your daughter on the stage.

Refrain 3

Don't put your daughter on the stage, Mrs Worthington,
Don't put your daughter on the stage,
Though they said at the school of acting
She was lovely as Peer Gynt,
I'm afraid on the whole
An ingénue role
Would emphasise her squint.
She's a big girl, and though her teeth are fairly good
She's not the type I ever would
Be eager to engage,
No more buts,
Mrs Worthington,
NUTS,
Mrs Worthington,
Don't put your daughter on the stage.

Refrain 4

Don't put your daughter on the stage, Mrs Worthington,
Don't put your daughter on the stage,
One look at her bandy legs should prove
She hasn't got a chance,
In addition to which

The son of a bitch
Can neither sing nor dance,
She's a *vile* girl and uglier than mortal sin,
One look at her has put me in
A tearing bloody rage,
That sufficed,
Mrs Worthington,
Christ!
Mrs Worthington,
Don't put your daughter on the stage.

After the success of Private Lives, Coward *and Gertrude Lawrence were reunited in a sequence of nine one-act plays under the title* Tonight at 8.30 *which they performed in London and New York during 1936 and 1937. One of the most popular was* Red Peppers, *a salute to the provincial music-hall, already threatened by the success of talking pictures.*

George and Lily Pepper squabble with each other backstage but unite when a manager or musical director dares to criticise their faded song and dance act. Coward wrote two original routines for them; the first is a mildly suggestive sailor number, typical of those 'lost Empires' . . . but only he could have worked a quotation from Alexander Pope into the last chorus.

Has Anybody Seen Our Ship?

Verse 1

What shall we do with the drunken sailor?
So the saying goes.
We're not tight but we're none too bright,
Great Scott! I don't suppose!
We've lost our way
And we've lost our pay,
And to make the thing complete,
We've been and gone and lost the bloomin' fleet!

Refrain 1

Has anybody seen our ship?
The H M S *Peculiar*.
We've been on shore
For a month or more,
And when we see the captain we shall get 'what for'.
Heave ho, me hearties,
Sing Glory Hallelujah,
A lady bold as she could be
Pinched our whistles at 'The Golden Key'.
Now we're in between the devil and the deep blue sea.
Has anybody seen our ship?

Verse 2

What's to be done with the girls on shore
Who lead our tars astray?
What's to be done with the drinks galore
That make them pass away?
We got wet ears
From our first five beers—
After that we lost control,
And now we find we're up the blinking pole!

Refrain 2

Has anybody seen our ship?
The H M S *Disgusting*.
We've three guns aft
And another one fore
And they've promised us a funnel for the next world war.
Heave ho, me hearties,
The quarterdeck needs dusting.
We had a binge last Christmas year,
Nice plum puddings and a round of beer,
But the captain pulled his cracker and we cried, 'Oh dear!'
Has anybody seen our ship?

Refrain 3

Has anybody seen our ship?
The H M S *Suggestive*.
She sailed away
Across the bay,
And we haven't had a smell of her since New Year's Day.
Heave ho, me hearties,
We're getting rather restive.
We pooled our money, spent the lot,
The world forgetting by the world forgot,
Now we haven't got a penny for the you know what!
Has anybody seen our ship?

The plays which make up Tonight at 8.30 *are seldom revived, but several of them have been filmed or adapted for television. One of them, originally entitled* Still Life, *was made into a classic British film in 1945. When it was published in a collection of his plays, Coward wrote:*

Still Life was the most mature play of the whole series . . . It is well written, economical and well constructed: the characters, I think, are true, and I can say now, reading it with detachment after so many years, that I am proud to have written it.

Coward wrote the screenplay for the film and produced it himself; the director was David Lean and the film was given a new title.

Saw very rough cut of *Brief Encounter*. Delighted with it. Celia [Johnson] quite wonderful; Trevor Howard fine and obviously a new star. Whole thing beautifully played and directed – and, let's face it, most beautifully written.

(*Diary, 2 June 1945*)

In 1956 Coward prepared a version for two voices and recorded it in New York with Margaret Leighton playing opposite him. This condensed version appears here, the only difference being that the original ending – which requires a third voice – has been restored.

134

BRIEF ENCOUNTER

Principals: LAURA JESSON, ALEC HARVEY, DOLLY MESSITER.

SCENE: *The action of the play takes place in the refreshment room of Milford Junction Station.*

SCENE 1

When the curtain rises it is about 5.25 p.m. on an evening in April. The evening sunlight streams through the right-hand window illuminating gaily the paraphernalia on the counter.

LAURA JESSON is sitting at the downstage table having tea. She is an attractive woman in the thirties. Her clothes are not particularly smart but obviously chosen with taste. She looks exactly what she is, a pleasant, ordinary married woman, rather pale, for she is not very strong, and with the definite charm of personality which comes from natural kindliness, humour and reasonable conscience. She is reading a Boots' library book at which she occasionally smiles. On the chair beside her there are several parcels as she has been shopping.

ALEC HARVEY enters. He is about thirty-five. He wears a moustache, a mackintosh and a squash hat, and he carries a small bag. His manner is decisive and unflurried. He takes off his hat and sits down. LAURA glances at the clock, collects her parcels in a leisurely manner and goes out on to the platform.

There is a rumbling noise in the distance, and the sound of a bell. Then a terrific clatter as the express roars through the station.

LAURA enters hurriedly holding a handkerchief to her eye. ALEC rises from his table and comes over.

ALEC: Can I help you?

LAURA: Oh, no, please – it's only something in my eye.

ALEC: Please let me look. I happen to be a doctor.

LAURA: It's very kind of you.

ALEC: Turn round to the light, please – now – look up – now look down – I can see it. Keep still— [*He twists up the corner of his handkerchief and rapidly operates with it.*] There—

LAURA [blinking]: Oh dear – what a relief – it was agonising.
ALEC: It looks like a bit of grit.
LAURA: It was when the express went through – thank you very much indeed—
ALEC: Not at all.
[There is the sound of a bell on the platform.]
LAURA: How lucky for me that you happened to be here.
ALEC: Anybody could have done it.
LAURA: Never mind, you did and I'm most grateful. There's my train. Goodbye.
[She puts out her hand and he shakes it politely. She goes out.
    ALEC looks after her for a moment and then goes back to his table. There is the noise of the train rumbling into the station as the lights fade.]

SCENE 2

Nearly three months have passed since the preceding scene, and it is now July.
    ALEC and LAURA come in. LAURA is wearing a summer dress, ALEC, a grey flannel suit.

ALEC: Tea or lemonade?
LAURA: Tea, I think – it's more refreshing, really.
[She sits down at the table by the door. ALEC goes to the counter.]
LAURA: Do you like milk in your tea?
ALEC: Yes, don't you?
LAURA: Yes – fortunately.
ALEC: Station refreshments are generally a wee bit arbitrary, you know.
LAURA: I wasn't grumbling.
ALEC [smiling]: Do you ever grumble – are you ever sullen and cross and bad-tempered?
LAURA: Of course I am – at least not sullen exactly – but I sometimes get into rages.
ALEC: I can't visualise you in a rage.

136

LAURA: I really don't see why you should.

ALEC: Oh, I don't know – there are signs, you know – one can usually tell—

LAURA: Long upper lips and jaw lines and eyes close together?

ALEC: You haven't any of those things.

LAURA: Do you feel guilty at all? I do.

ALEC [smiling]: Guilty?

LAURA: You ought to more than me, really – you neglected your work this afternoon.

ALEC: I worked this morning – a little relaxation never did anyone any harm. Why should either of us feel guilty?

LAURA: I don't know – a sort of instinct – as though we were letting something happen that oughtn't to happen.

ALEC: How awfully nice you are!

LAURA: When I was a child in Cornwall – we lived in Cornwall, you know – May, that's my sister, and I used to climb out of our bedroom window on summer nights and go down to the cove and bathe. It was dreadfully cold but we felt very adventurous. I'd never have dared do it by myself, but sharing the danger made it all right – that's how I feel now, really.

ALEC: Have a bun – it's awfully bad for you.

LAURA: You're laughing at me!

ALEC: Yes, a little, but I'm laughing at myself, too.

LAURA: Why?

ALEC: For feeling a small pang when you said about being guilty.

LAURA: There you are, you see!

ALEC: We haven't done anything wrong.

LAURA: Of course we haven't.

ALEC: An accidental meeting – then another accidental meeting – then a little lunch – then the movies – what could be more ordinary? More natural?

LAURA: We're adults, after all.

ALEC: I never see myself as an adult, do you?

LAURA [firmly]: Yes, I do. I'm a respectable married woman with a husband and a home and three children.

ALEC: But there must be a part of you, deep down inside, that doesn't feel like that at all – some little spirit that still wants to

137

climb out of the window – that still longs to splash about a bit in the dangerous sea.

LAURA: Perhaps we none of us ever grow up entirely.

ALEC: How awfully nice you are!

LAURA: You said that before.

ALEC: I thought perhaps you hadn't heard.

LAURA: I heard all right.

ALEC [*gently*]: I'm respectable too, you know. I have a home and a wife and children and responsibilities – I also have a lot of work to do and a lot of ideals all mixed up with it.

LAURA: What's she like?

ALEC: Madeleine?

LAURA: Yes.

ALEC: Small, dark, rather delicate—

LAURA: How funny! I should have thought she'd be fair.

ALEC: And your husband? What's he like?

LAURA: Medium height, brown hair, kindly, unemotional and not delicate at all.

ALEC: You said that proudly.

LAURA: Did I? [*She looks down.*]

ALEC: What's the matter?

LAURA: The matter? What could be the matter?

ALEC: You suddenly went away.

LAURA [*brightly*]: I thought perhaps we were being rather silly.

ALEC: Why?

LAURA: Oh, I don't know – we are such complete strangers, really.

ALEC: It's one thing to close a window, but quite another to slam it down on my fingers.

LAURA: I'm sorry.

ALEC: Please come back again.

LAURA: Is tea bad for one? Worse than coffee, I mean?

ALEC [*laughing*]: If this is a professional interview, my fee is a guinea.

LAURA [*laughing*]: It's nearly time for your train.

ALEC: I hate to think of it, chugging along, interrupting our tea party.

LAURA: I really am sorry now.

ALEC: What for?

LAURA: For being disagreeable.

ALEC: I don't think you could be disagreeable.

LAURA: You said something just now about your work and ideals being mixed up with it – what ideals?

ALEC: That's a long story.

LAURA: I suppose all doctors ought to have ideals, really – otherwise I should think the work would be unbearable.

ALEC: Surely you're not encouraging me to talk shop?

LAURA: Do you come here every Thursday?

ALEC: Yes. I come in from Churley, and spend a day in the hospital. Stephen Lynn graduated with me – he's the chief physician here. I take over from him once a week, it gives him a chance to go up to London and me a chance to observe and study the hospital patients.

LAURA: Is that a great advantage?

ALEC: Of course. You see I have a special pigeon.

LAURA: What is it?

ALEC: Preventive medicine.

LAURA: Oh, I see.

ALEC [laughing]: I'm afraid you don't.

LAURA: I was trying to be intelligent.

ALEC: Most good doctors, especially when they're young, have private dreams – that's the best part of them, sometimes though, those get over-professionalised and strangulated and – am I boring you?

LAURA: No – I don't quite understand – but you're not boring me.

ALEC: What I mean is this – all good doctors must be primarily enthusiasts. They must have, like writers and painters, and priests, a sense of vocation – a deep-rooted, unsentimental desire to do good.

LAURA: Yes – I see that.

ALEC: Well, obviously one way of preventing disease is worth fifty ways of curing it – that's where my ideal comes in – preventive medicine isn't anything to do with medicine at all, really – it's concerned with conditions, living conditions and common-sense and hygiene. For instance, my speciality is pneumoconiosis.

LAURA: Oh dear!

ALEC: Don't be alarmed, it's simpler than it sounds – it's nothing but a slow process of fibrosis of the lung due to the inhalation of particles of dust. In the hospital here there are splendid opportunities for observing cures and making notes, because of the coal mines.

LAURA: You suddenly look much younger.

ALEC [*brought up short*]: Do I?

LAURA: Almost like a little boy.

ALEC: What made you say that?

LAURA [*staring at him*]: I don't know – yes, I do.

ALEC [*gently*]: Tell me.

LAURA [*with panic in her voice*]: Oh, no – I couldn't really. You were saying about the coal mines—

ALEC [*looking into her eyes*]: Yes – the inhalation of coal dust – that's one specific form of the diseases – it's called Anthracosis.

LAURA [*hypnotised*]: What are the others?

ALEC: Chalicosis – that comes from metal dust – steel works, you know—

LAURA: Yes, of course. Steel works.

ALEC: And Silicosis – stone dust – that's gold mines.

LAURA [*almost in a whisper*]: I see.

[*There is the sound of a bell.*]

There's your train.

ALEC [*looking down*]: Yes.

LAURA: You mustn't miss it.

ALEC: No.

LAURA [*again the panic in her voice*]: What's the matter?

ALEC [*with an effort*]: Nothing – nothing at all.

LAURA [*socially*]: It's been so very nice – I've enjoyed my afternoon enormously.

ALEC: I'm so glad – so have I. I apologise for boring you with those long medical words—

LAURA: I feel dull and stupid, not to be able to understand more.

ALEC: Shall I see you again?

[*There is the sound of a train approaching.*]

LAURA: It's the other platform, isn't it? You'll have to run. Don't worry about me – mine's due in a few minutes.

ALEC: Shall I see you again?

LAURA: Of course – perhaps you could come over to Ketchworth one Sunday. It's rather far, I know, but we should be delighted to see you.

ALEC [*intensely*]: Please – please—

[*The train is heard drawing to a standstill.*]

LAURA: What is it?

ALEC: Next Thursday – the same time—

LAURA: No – I can't possibly – I—

ALEC: Please – I ask you most humbly—

LAURA: You'll miss your train!

ALEC: All right. [*He gets up.*]

LAURA: Run—

ALEC [*taking her hand*]: Goodbye.

LAURA [*breathlessly*]: I'll be there.

ALEC: Thank you, my dear.

[*He goes out at a run.*

LAURA *sits quite still staring in front of her as the lights fade.*]

SCENE 3

It is now October. Three months have passed since the preceding scene. Alec and Laura are at their usual table.

ALEC: I didn't mean to be unkind.

LAURA: It doesn't matter.

ALEC: We can't part like this.

LAURA: I think it would be better if we did.

ALEC: You don't really mean that?

LAURA: I'm trying to mean it – I'm trying with all my strength.

ALEC: O my dearest dear—

LAURA: Don't – please don't—

ALEC: It's no use running away from the truth, darling – we're lovers, aren't we? If it happens or if it doesn't, we're lovers in our hearts.

141

LAURA: Can't you see how wrong it is? How dreadfully wrong!

ALEC: I can see what's true – whether it's wrong or right. [*Urgently*] There's no chance of Stephen getting back until late – nobody need ever know.

LAURA: It's so furtive to love like that – so cheap – much better not to love at all.

ALEC: It's too late not to love at all – be brave – we're both in the same boat – let's be generous to each other.

LAURA: What is there brave in it – sneaking away to someone else's house, loving in secret with the horror of being found out hanging over us all the time. It would be far braver to say goodbye and never see each other again.

ALEC: Could you be as brave as that? I know I couldn't.

LAURA [*breathlessly*]: Couldn't you?

ALEC: Listen, my dear. This is something that's never happened to either of us before. We've loved before and been happy before, and miserable and contented and reckless, but this is different – something lovely and strange and desperately difficult. We can't measure it along with the values of our ordinary lives.

LAURA: Why should it be so important – why should we let it be so important?

ALEC: We can't help ourselves.

LAURA: We can – we can if only we're strong enough.

ALEC: Why is it so strong to deny something that's urgent and real – something that all our instincts are straining after – mightn't it be weak and not strong at all to run away from such tremendous longing?

LAURA: Is it so real to you? So tremendous?

ALEC: Can't you see that it is?

LAURA: It's so difficult, so strained. I'm lost.

ALEC: Don't say that, darling.

LAURA: Loving you is hard for me – it makes me a stranger in my own house. Familiar things, ordinary things that I've known for years, like the dining-room curtains, and the wooden tub with a silver top that holds biscuits, and a water-colour of San Remo that my mother painted, look odd to me, as though they belonged to someone else – when I've just left

142

you, when I go home, I'm more lonely than I've ever been before. I passed the house the other day without noticing and had to turn back, and when I went in it seemed to draw away from me – my whole life seems to be drawing away from me, and – and I don't know what to do.

ALEC: O darling—

LAURA: I love them just the same, Fred I mean and the children, but it's as though it wasn't me at all – as though I were looking on at someone else. Do you know what I mean? Is it the same with you? Or is it easier for men—

ALEC: I don't know.

LAURA: Please, dear, don't look unhappy. I'm not grumbling, really I'm not—

ALEC: I don't suppose being in love has ever been easy for anybody.

LAURA [reaching for his hand]: We've only got a few more minutes – I didn't mean to be depressing.

ALEC: It isn't any easier for me, darling, honestly it isn't.

LAURA: I know, I know – I only wanted reassuring.

ALEC: I hold you in my arms all the way back in the train – I'm angry with every moment that I'm not alone – to love you uninterrupted – whenever my surgery door opens and a patient comes in, my heart jumps in case it might be you. One of them I'm grateful to – he's got neuritis, and I give him sun-ray treatment – he lies quite quietly baking, and I can be with you in the shadows behind the lamp.

LAURA: How silly we are – how unbearably silly!

ALEC: Friday – Saturday – Sunday – Monday – Tuesday – Wednesday—

LAURA: Thursday—

ALEC: It's all right, isn't it?

LAURA: Oh, yes – of course it is.

ALEC: Don't pass the house again – don't let it snub you. Go boldly in and stare that damned water-colour out of countenance.

LAURA: All right – don't bake your poor neuritis man too long – you might blister him.

[There is the sound of a train drawing into the station.]

143

LAURA: There's your train.

ALEC: I'm going to miss it.

LAURA: Please go.

ALEC: No.

LAURA [*clasping and unclasping her hands*]: I wish I could think clearly. I wish I could know – really know what to do.

ALEC: Do you trust me?

LAURA: Yes – I trust you.

ALEC: I don't mean conventionally – I mean really.

LAURA: Yes.

ALEC: Everything's against us – all the circumstances of our lives – those have got to go on unaltered. We're nice people, you and I, and we've got to go on being nice. Let's enclose this love of ours with real strength, and let that strength be that no one is hurt by it except ourselves.

LAURA: Must we be hurt by it?

ALEC: Yes – when the time comes.

LAURA: Very well.

ALEC: All the furtiveness and the secrecy and the hole-in-corner cheapness can be justified if only we're strong enough – strong enough to keep it to ourselves, clean and untouched by anybody else's knowledge or even suspicion – something of our own for ever – to be remembered—

LAURA: Very well.

ALEC: We won't speak of it any more – I'm going now – back to Stephen's flat. I'll wait for you – if you don't come I shall know only that you weren't quite ready – that you needed a little longer to find your own dear heart. This is the address.

[*He scribbles on a bit of paper as the express thunders through the station. He gets up and goes swiftly without looking at her again. She sits staring at the paper, then she fumbles in her bag and finds a cigarette. She lights it – the platform bell goes.*

There is the noise of the 5.43 – LAURA'*s train – steaming into the station.* LAURA *sits puffing her cigarette. Suddenly she gets up – gathers up her bag quickly, and moves towards the door. She pauses and comes back to the table as the whistle blows. The train starts, she puts the paper in her bag and goes quietly out as the lights fade.*]

144

SCENE 4

The time is about 9.45 on an evening in December. There are only two lights on in the refreshment room as it is nearly closing time.

When the scene starts LAURA *is sitting alone. There is the noise of a fast train rattling through the station.* ALEC *comes in – he looks hopelessly round for a moment, and then sees her.*

ALEC: Thank God – O darling!

LAURA: Please go away – please don't say anything.

ALEC: I can't let you go like this.

LAURA: You must. It'll be better – really it will.

ALEC [*sitting down beside her*]: You're being dreadfully cruel.

LAURA: I feel so utterly degraded.

ALEC: It was just a beastly accident that he came back early – he doesn't know who you are – he never even saw you.

LAURA: I listened to your voices in the sitting-room – I crept out and down the stairs – feeling like a prostitute.

ALEC: Don't, dearest – don't talk like that, please—

LAURA [*bitterly*]: I suppose he laughed, didn't he – after he got over being annoyed? I suppose you spoke of me together as men of the world.

ALEC: We didn't speak of you – we spoke of a nameless creature who had no reality at all.

LAURA [*wildly*]: Why didn't you tell him the truth? Why didn't you say who I was and that we were lovers – shameful secret lovers – using his flat like a bad house because we had nowhere else to go, and were afraid of being found out! Why didn't you tell him we were cheap and low and without courage – why didn't you—

ALEC: Stop it, Laura – pull yourself together!

LAURA: It's true – don't you see, it's true!

ALEC: It's nothing of the sort. I know you feel horrible, and I'm deeply, desperately sorry. I feel horrible, too, but it doesn't matter really – this – this unfortunate, damnable incident – it was just bad luck. It couldn't affect us really, you and me – we know the truth – we know we really love each other – that's all that matters.

145

LAURA: It isn't all that matters – other things matter, too, self-respect matters, and decency – I can't go on any longer.

ALEC: Could you really – say goodbye – not see me any more?

LAURA: Yes – if you'd help me.

[*There is silence for a moment.* ALEC *gets up and walks about – he stops and stands staring at a coloured calendar on the wall.*]

ALEC [*quietly, with his back to her*]: I love you, Laura – I shall love you always until the end of my life – all the shame that the world might force on us couldn't touch the real truth of it. I can't look at you now because I know something – I know that this is the beginning of the end – not the end of my loving you – but the end of our being together. But not quite yet, darling – please not quite yet.

LAURA: Very well – not quite yet.

ALEC: I know what you feel – about this evening, I mean – about the beastliness of it. I know about the strain of our different lives, our lives apart from each other. The feeling of guilt – of doing wrong is a little too strong, isn't it? Too persistent – perhaps too great a price to pay for the few hours of happiness we get out of it. I know all this because it's the same for me, too.

LAURA: You can look at me now – I'm all right.

ALEC [*turning*]: Let's be careful – let's prepare ourselves – a sudden break now, however brave and admirable, would be too cruel – we can't do such violence to our hearts and minds.

LAURA: Very well.

ALEC: I'm going away.

LAURA: I see.

ALEC: But not quite yet.

LAURA: Please not quite yet.

ALEC: I want you to promise me something.

LAURA: What is it?

ALEC: Promise me that however unhappy you are, and however much you think things over, that you'll meet me next Thursday as usual.

LAURA: Not at the flat.

ALEC: No – be at the Picture House café at the same time. I'll hire a car – we'll drive out into the country.

LAURA: All right – I promise.

ALEC: We've got to talk – I've got to explain.

LAURA: About going away?

ALEC: Yes.

LAURA: Where are you going? Where can you go? You can't give up your practice!

ALEC: I've had a job offered me – I wasn't going to tell you – I wasn't going to take it – but I must – I know now, it's the only way out.

LAURA: Where?

ALEC: A long way away – Johannesburg.

LAURA [hopelessly]: O God!

ALEC [hurriedly]: My brother's out there – they're opening a new hospital – they want me in it. It's a fine opportunity, really. I'll take Madeleine and the boys. It's been torturing me for three weeks, the necessity of making a decision one way or the other – I haven't told anybody, not even Madeleine. I couldn't bear the idea of leaving you, but now I see – it's got to happen soon, anyway – it's almost happening already.

LAURA [tonelessly]: When will you go?

ALEC: In about two months' time.

LAURA: It's quite near, isn't it?

ALEC: Do you want me to stay? Do you want me to turn down the offer?

LAURA: Don't be foolish, Alec.

ALEC: I'll do whatever you say.

LAURA: That's unkind of you, my darling. [She suddenly buries her head in her arms and bursts into tears.]

ALEC [putting his arms round her]: O Laura, don't, please don't!

LAURA: I'll be all right – leave me alone a minute.

ALEC: I love you – I love you.

LAURA: I know.

ALEC: We knew we'd get hurt.

LAURA [sitting up]: I'm being very stupid.

ALEC [giving her his handkerchief]: Here.

LAURA [blowing her nose]: Thank you.

[The platform bell goes.]

There's my train.

ALEC: You're not angry with me, are you?

LAURA: No, I'm not angry – I don't think I'm anything, really – I feel just tired.

ALEC: Forgive me.

LAURA: Forgive you for what?

ALEC: For everything – for having met you in the first place – for taking the piece of grit out of your eye – for loving you – for bringing you so much misery.

LAURA [*trying to smile*]: I'll forgive you – if you'll forgive me—
    [*There is the noise of a train pulling into the station.* LAURA *and* ALEC *get up.*]

ALEC: I'll see you into the train.

LAURA: No – please stay here.

ALEC: All right.

LAURA [*softly*]: Good-night, darling.

ALEC: Good-night, darling.
    [*She goes hurriedly out on to the platform without looking back.*]

SCENE 5

The time is between 5 and 5.30 on an afternoon in March.

ALEC: Are you all right, darling?

LAURA: Yes, I'm all right.

ALEC: I wish I could think of something to say.

LAURA: It doesn't matter – not saying anything, I mean.

ALEC: I'll miss my train and wait to see you into yours.

LAURA: No – no – please don't. I'll come over to your platform with you – I'd rather.

ALEC: Very well.

LAURA: Do you think we shall ever see each other again?

ALEC: I don't know. [*His voice breaks.*] Not for years, anyway.

LAURA: The children will all be grown up – I wonder if they'll ever meet and know each other.

ALEC: Couldn't I write to you – just once in a while?

LAURA: No – please not – we promised we wouldn't.

ALEC: Please know this – please know that you'll be with me for ages and ages yet – far away into the future. Time will wear down the agony of not seeing you, bit by bit the pain will go – but the loving you and the memory of you won't ever go – please know that.

LAURA: I know it.

ALEC: It's easier for me than for you. I do realise that, really I do. I at least will have different shapes to look at, and new work to do – you have to go on among familiar things – my heart aches for you so.

LAURA: I'll be all right.

ALEC: I love you with all my heart and soul.

LAURA [*quietly*]: I want to die – if only I could die.

ALEC: If you died you'd forget me – I want to be remembered.

LAURA: Yes, I know – I do, too.

ALEC: Goodbye, my dearest love.

LAURA: Goodbye, my dearest love.

ALEC: We've still got a few minutes.

LAURA: Thank God—!

[DOLLY MESSITER *bustles into the refreshment room. She is a nicely dressed woman, with rather a fussy manner. She is laden with parcels. She sees* LAURA.]

DOLLY: Laura! What a lovely surprise!

LAURA [*dazed*]: Oh, Dolly!

DOLLY: My dear, I've been shopping till I'm dropping – that sounds like a song, doesn't it? My feet are nearly falling off, and my throat's parched. I thought of having tea in Spindle's, but I was terrified of losing the train. I'm always missing trains, and being late for meals, and Bob gets disagreeable for days at a time. Oh dear – [*She flops down at their table.*]

LAURA: This is Dr Harvey.

ALEC [*rising*]: How do you do!

DOLLY [*shaking hands*]: How do you do! Would you be a perfect dear and get me a cup of tea! I don't think I could drag my poor old bones as far as the counter. I must get some chocolates for Tony, too, but I can do that afterwards – here's sixpence—

ALEC [*waving it away*]: No, please—

[*He goes drearily over to the counter, gets another cup of tea and comes back to the table, meanwhile* DOLLY *continues to talk.*]

DOLLY: My dear – what a nice-looking man. Who on earth is he? Really, you're quite a dark horse. I shall telephone Fred in the morning and make mischief – that is a bit of luck. I haven't seen you for ages, and I've been meaning to pop in, but Tony's had measles, you know, and I had all that awful fuss about Phyllis – but of course you don't know – she left me! Suddenly upped and went, my dear, without even an hour's warning, let alone a month's notice.

LAURA [*with an effort*]: Oh, how dreadful!

DOLLY: Mind you, I never cared for her much, but still Tony did. Tony adored her, and – but, never mind, I'll tell you all about that in the train.

[ALEC *arrives back at the table with her tea – he sits down again.*] Thank you so very much. They've certainly put enough milk in it – but still it's wet and that's all one can really ask for in a refreshment room— [*She sips it.*] Oh dear – no sugar.

ALEC: It's in the spoon.

DOLLY: Oh, of course – what a fool I am – Laura, you look frightfully well. I do wish I'd known you were coming in today, we could have come together and lunched and had a good gossip. I loathe shopping by myself, anyway.

[*There is the sound of a bell on the platform.*]

LAURA: There's your train.

ALEC: Yes, I know.

DOLLY: Aren't you coming with us?

ALEC: No, I go in the opposite direction. My practice is in Churley.

DOLLY: How interesting! What sort of a doctor are you? I mean, are you a specialist at anything or just a sort of general family doctor?

ALEC: I'm a general practitioner at the moment.

LAURA [*dully*]: Dr Harvey is going out to Africa next week.

DOLLY: But, my dear, how thrilling! Are you going to operate on the Zulus or something? I always associate Africa with Zulus, but I may be quite wrong.

[*There is the sound of* ALEC'*s train approaching.*]

ALEC: I must go.

LAURA: Yes, you must.

ALEC: Goodbye.

DOLLY: Goodbye.

[*He shakes hands with* DOLLY, *looks at* LAURA *swiftly once, then presses her hand under cover of the table and leaves hurriedly as the train is heard rumbling into the station.* LAURA *sits quite still.*]

DOLLY: He'll have to run – he's got to get right over to the other platform. How did you meet him?

LAURA: I got something in my eye one day, and he took it out.

DOLLY: My dear – how very romantic! I'm always getting things in my eye and nobody the least bit attractive has ever paid the faintest attention – which reminds me – you know about Harry and Lucy Jenner, don't you?

LAURA [*listening for the train to start*]: No – what about them?

DOLLY: My dear – they're going to get a divorce – at least I believe they're getting a conjugal separation, or whatever it is to begin with, and the divorce later on.

[*The train starts, and the sound of it dies gradually away in the distance.*]

It seems that there's an awful Mrs Something or other in London that he's been carrying on with for ages – you know how he was always having to go up on business. Well, apparently Lucy's sister saw them, Harry and this woman, in the Tate Gallery of all places, and she wrote to Lucy, and then gradually the whole thing came out.

[*There is the sound of a bell on the platform.*]

Is that our train?

LAURA: The boat train.

DOLLY: Oh, yes – that doesn't stop, does it? Express trains are Tony's passion in life – he knows them all by name – where they start from and where they go to, and how long they take to get there. Oh dear, I mustn't forget his chocolate. [*She jumps up and goes to the counter.*]

[LAURA *remains quite still. The express is heard in the distance.* LAURA *suddenly gets up and goes swiftly out on to the platform. The express roars through the station as* DOLLY *finishes buying and paying for her chocolate.* LAURA *comes in again, looking very white and shaky.*]

DOLLY: My dear, I couldn't think where you'd disappeared to.

LAURA: I just wanted to see the express go through.

DOLLY: What on earth's the matter – do you feel ill?
LAURA: I'm all right, really.
    [*The platform bell goes.*]
  That's our train.
    [DOLLY *proceeds to gather up her parcels as—*]

THE CURTAIN FALLS

The second volume of Coward's autobiography, Past Conditional, *ends in 1933 and the third,* Future Indefinite, *starts in 1939. So* Operette, *which opened in 1938 to a poor reception, is denied the author's own analysis of its failure. Writing in the* Sunday Times, *James Agate said, 'I see nothing in* Operette *that was not brought better off either in* Bitter Sweet, *or* Cavalcade, *or* Words and Music, *or* Conversation Piece, *or* Tonight at 8.30 . . . *This is trite.'*

In an effort to salute any positive aspects of the production that he could find, Agate paid extravagant compliments to Gladys Calthrop's decor and Irene Vanbrugh's performance, but he was deaf to its one permanently resounding hit. Connoisseurs of Coward's skill at quotation will enjoy identifying the snatches of Walter Savage Landor, Scott and W. E. Henley as well, of course, as Mrs Hemans who provided the title . . .

The Stately Homes of England

Verse 1

Lord Elderley, Lord Borrowmere,
Lord Sickert and Lord Camp
With every virtue, every grace,
Ah what avails the sceptred race,
Here you see – the four of us,
And there are so many more of us
Eldest sons that must succeed.
We know how Caesar conquered Gaul

And how to whack a cricket ball;
Apart from this, our education
Lacks co-ordination.
Though we're young and tentative
And rather rip-representative,
Scions of a noble breed,
We are the products of those homes serene and stately
Which only lately
Seem to have run to seed!

Refrain 1

The Stately Homes of England,
How beautiful they stand,
To prove the upper classes
Have still the upper hand;
Though the fact that they have to be rebuilt
And frequently mortgaged to the hilt
Is inclined to take the gilt
Off the gingerbread,
And certainly damps the fun
Of the eldest son—
But still we won't be beaten,
We'll scrimp and scrape and save,
The playing fields of Eton
Have made us frightfully brave—
And though if the Van Dycks have to go
And we pawn the Bechstein Grand,
We'll stand
By the Stately Homes of England.

Verse 2

Here you see
The pick of us,
You may be heartily sick of us,
Still with sense
We're all imbued.
Our homes command extensive views
And with assistance from the Jews

We have been able to dispose of
Rows and rows and rows of
Gainsboroughs and Lawrences,
Some sporting prints of Aunt Florence's,
Some of which were rather rude.
Although we sometimes flaunt our family conventions,
Our good intentions
Mustn't be misconstrued.

Refrain 2

The Stately Homes of England
We proudly represent,
We only keep them up for
Americans to rent.
Though the pipes that supply the bathroom burst
And the lavatory makes you fear the worst,
It was used by Charles the First
Quite informally,
And later by George the Fourth
On a journey north.
The State Apartments keep their
Historical renown,
It's wiser not to sleep there
In case they tumble down;
But still if they ever catch on fire
Which, with any luck, they might
We'll fight
For the Stately Homes of England.

Refrain 3

The Stately Homes of England,
Though rather in the lurch,
Provide a lot of chances
For Psychical Research—
There's the ghost of a crazy younger son
Who murdered, in thirteen fifty-one,
An extremely rowdy Nun
Who resented it,

And people who come to call
Meet her in the hall.
The baby in the guest wing,
Who crouches by the grate,
Was walled up in the west wing
In fourteen twenty-eight.
If anyone spots
The Queen of Scots
In a hand-embroidered shroud
We're proud
Of the Stately Homes of England.

REPRISE – ACT II

Verse 3

Lord Elderley, Lord Borrowmere,
Lord Sickert and Lord Camp,
Behold us in our hours of ease,
Uncertain, coy and hard to please.
Reading in Debrett of us,
This fine Patrician quartette of us,
We can feel extremely proud,
Our ancient lineage we trace
Back to the cradle of the Race
Before those beastly Roman bowmen
Bitched our local Yeomen.
Though the new democracy
May pain the old Aristocracy
We've not winced nor cried aloud,
Under the bludgeonings of chance what will be – will be.
Our heads will still be
Bloody but quite unbowed!

Refrain 4

The Stately Homes of England
In valley, dale and glen
Produce a race of charming,
Innocuous young men.

Though our mental equipment may be slight
And we barely distinguish left from right,
We are quite prepared to fight
For our principles,
Though none of us know so far
What they really are.
Our duty to the nation,
It's only fair to state,
Lies not in procreation
But what we procreate;
And so we can cry
With kindling eye
As to married life we go,
What ho!
For the Stately Homes of England!

Refrain 5

The Stately Homes of England,
Although a trifle bleak,
Historically speaking,
Are more or less unique,
We've a cousin who won the Golden Fleece
And a very peculiar fowling-piece
Which was sent to Cromwell's niece,
Who detested it,
And rapidly sent it back
With a dirty crack.
A note we have from Chaucer
Contains a bawdy joke.
We also have a saucer
That Bloody Mary broke.
We've two pairs of tights
King Arthur's Knights
Had completely worn away.
Sing Hey!
For the Stately Homes of England!

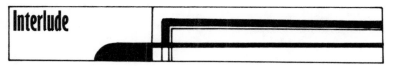

After the bruising reception of Operette, Noël Coward turned his attention to writing of another kind. He had made his mark as a composer of words and music, as a straight playwright and as the author of a successful autobiography. Now he produced the first of his volumes of short stories. Over the next thirty years he published twenty short stories in all and, in 1960, a comic novel, Pomp and Circumstance.

These were not merely a refuge from critical disdain. They were, like his verse and his painting, other strings to a particularly flexible bow. Nearly all of his stories reflect some aspect of his life or travels about which he felt passionately. The two which appear here have, in common with nearly half the full score, a background in the professional theatre.

Cheap Excursion

Jimmy said, 'Good-night, Miss Reed', as she passed him in the passage. He did it ordinarily, no overtones or undertones, not the slightest indication of any secret knowledge between them, not even a glint in his eye, nothing beyond the correct subservience of an assistant stage manager to a star. She answered him vaguely, that well-known gracious smile, and went on to the stage door, her heart pounding violently as though someone had sprung at her out of the dark.

In the car, she sat very still with her hands folded in her lap, vainly hoping that this very stillness, this stern outward quietness might help to empty her mind. Presently she gave up and watched herself carefully taking a cigarette out of her case and lighting it. 'I am Diana Reed. *The* Diana Reed, lighting a cigarette. I am Diana Reed driving home in my expensive car to my expensive flat – I am tired after my performance and as I have a matinée tomorrow it is sane and sensible for me to go straight home to bed after the show. I am having supper with Jimmy tomorrow night and probably Friday night, too – there are hundreds of other nights and there is no reason whatsoever for me to feel lonely and agonised and without peace. I am Diana Reed – I am celebrated, successful, sought after – my play is a hit – my notices were excellent – except for the *Sunday Times*. I am Diana Reed, famous, nearing forty and desperate. I am in love, not perhaps really in love like I was with Tony, nor even Pierre Chabron, but that was different, because it lasted such a little time and was foreign and mixed up with being abroad and everything, but I am in love all right and it's different again, it's always different and always difficult, and I wish to God I could be happy with it and give up to it, but there's too much to remember and too much to be careful of and too many people wanting to find out about it and gossip and smear it with their dirty fingers.'

She let down the window and flicked her cigarette on to the pavement. It fell at the feet of a man in a mackintosh and a bowler hat; he looked up quickly and she drew herself back guiltily into the corner of the car. When she let herself into her flat and switched on the lights in the sitting-room its smug tidy emptiness seemed to jeer at her. It was a charming room. The furniture was good, plain and luxuriously simple in line. There was the small Utrillo that Tony had given her so many years ago – it had been in her flat in Cavendish Street for ages, and she had even taken it on tour with her. That sharp sunny little street with the pinkish-white walls and neat row of plane trees making shadows across the road. The only other picture in the room was a Marie Laurencin of a woman in a sort of turban. It was quite small and framed in glass. That she had bought herself a couple of years ago when she was in Paris with Barbara and Nicky. Nicky said it looked like a very pale peach with currants in it.

She pitched her hat on to the sofa where it lay looking apologetic, almost cringing, and went over and opened the window. Outside it was very quiet, only dark rooftops and an occasional light here and there, but there was a glow in the sky over Oxford Street, and she could hear the noise of traffic far away muffled by the houses and squares in between. Just round the corner in George Street she heard a taxi stop, the slam of its door and the sharp ping as the driver shut off the meter. It might so easily be Jimmy, knowing that she was coming home alone, knowing how happy it would make her if he just came along for ten minutes to say good-night. The taxi with a grind of its gears started up and drove away, she could hear it for quite a while until there was silence again. It might still be Jimmy, he wouldn't be so extravagant as to keep a taxi waiting – he might at this very moment be coming up in a lift. In a few seconds she would hear the lift doors opening and then the front-door bell. She listened, holding her breath. He might, of course, come up the stairs in order not to be seen by the lift-man. Jimmy was nothing if not cautious. She waited, holding on to the windowsill tight to prevent herself from going to the front door. There was no sound, and presently her tension relaxed and, after rather a disdainful glance at herself in the glass over the mantelpiece, she went and opened the front door anyhow. The landing was deserted. When she came back into the room again she discovered, to her great irritation, that she was trembling.

She sat on a chair by the door, bolt upright, like somebody in a dentist's waiting-room. It wouldn't have surprised her if a bright, professionally smiling nurse had suddenly appeared and announced that Dr Martin was ready for her. Again she folded her hands in her lap. Someone had once told her that if you sat still as death with your hands relaxed, all the vitality ran out of the ends of your fingers and your nerves stopped being strained and tied up in knots. The Frigidaire in the kitchen suddenly gave a little click and started whirring. She stared at various things in the room, as though by concentrating, identifying herself with them she could become part of them and not feel so alone. The pickled wood Steinway with a pile of highly-coloured American tunes on it; the low table in front of the fire with last week's *Sketch* and *Bystander*, and the week before last's *New Yorker*, symmetrically arranged with this morning's *Daily Telegraph* folded neatly on top; the Chinese horse on the mantelpiece, very aloof and graceful with its front hoof raised as though it were just about to stamp on something small and insignificant. Nicky had said it was 'Ming' and Eileen had sworn it was 'Sung' because she had once been to China on a cruise and became superior at the mention of anything remotely oriental.

There had been quite a scene about it, culminating in Martha saying loudly that she'd settle for it being 'Gong' or 'Pong' if only everybody would bloody well shut up arguing and give her a drink.

Diana remembered how Jimmy had laughed, he was sitting on the floor next to Barbara. She looked at the empty space in front of the fireplace and saw him clearly, laughing, with his head thrown back and the firelight shining on his hair. That was during rehearsals, before anything had happened, before the opening night in Manchester and the fatal supper party at the Midland, when he had come over from his party at the other end of the French restaurant to tell her about the rehearsal for cuts the next afternoon. She remembered asking him to sit down and have a glass of champagne, and how politely he had accepted with a rather quizzical smile, almost an air of resignation. Then the long discussion about Duse and Bernhardt, and Jonathan getting excited and banging the table, and Jimmy sitting exactly opposite her where she could watch him out of the corner of her eye, listening intently to the conversation and twiddling the stem of his wine glass. They had all been dressed, of course. Jonathan and Mary had come up from London especially for the first night, also Violet and Dick and Maureen. Jimmy was wearing a grey flannel suit and a blue shirt and navy blue tie; occasionally the corners of his mouth twitched as though he were secretly amused, but didn't want to betray it. Then he had caught her looking at him, raised his eyebrows just for the fraction of a second and, with the most disarming friendliness, patted her hand. 'You gave a brilliant performance tonight,' he said. 'I felt very proud to be there.' That was the moment. That was the spark being struck. If she had had any sense she'd have run like a stag, but instead of running, instead of recognising danger, there she had sat idiotically smiling, warmed and attracted. Not content with having had a successful first night and having given a good performance, not satisfied with the fact that her friends, her close intimate friends had trailed all the way from London to enjoy her triumph with her, she had had to reach out greedily for something more. Well, God knows she'd got it all right. Here it was, all the fun of the fair. The fruits of those few weeks of determined fascination. She remembered, with a slight shudder, how very much at her best she had been, how swiftly she had

160

responded to her new audience, this nice-looking, physically attractive young man at least ten years younger than herself. How wittily she had joined in the general conversation. She remembered Jonathan laughing until he cried at the way she had described the dress rehearsal of *Lady from the East*, when the Japanese bridge had broken in the middle of her love scene. All the time, through all the laughter, through all the easy intimate jokes, she had had her eye on Jimmy, watching for his response, drawing him into the circle, appraising him, noting his slim wrists, the way he put his head on one side when he asked a question, his eyes, his thick eyelashes, his wide, square shoulders. She remembered saying 'good-night' to him with the others as they all went up in the lift together. Her suite was on the second floor, so she got out first. He was up on the top floor somewhere, sharing a room with Bob Harley, one of the small-part actors. She remembered, also, looking at herself in the glass in her bathroom and wondering, while she creamed her face, how attractive she was to him really, or how much of it was star glamour and position. Even then, so early in the business, she had begun to doubt. It was inevitable, of course, that doubt, particularly with someone younger than herself, more particularly still when that someone was assistant stage manager and general understudy. A few days after that, she had boldly asked him to supper in her suite. She remembered at the time being inwardly horrified at such flagrant indiscretion; however, no one had found out or even suspected. He accepted with alacrity, arrived a little late, having had a bath and changed his suit, and that was that.

Suddenly, the telephone bell rang. Diana jumped, and with a sigh of indescribable relief, went into her bedroom to answer it. Nobody but Jimmy knew that she was coming home early – nobody else would dream of finding her in at this time of night. She sat on the edge of the bed just in order to let it ring once more, just to give herself time to control the foolish happiness in her voice. Then she lifted the receiver and said 'Hallo', in exactly the right tone of politeness only slightly touched with irritation. She heard Martha's voice at the other end, and the suddenness of the disappointment robbed her of all feeling for a moment. She sat there rigid and cold with a dead heart. 'My God,' Martha was saying, 'you could knock me down with a crowbar, I couldn't be more surprised. I rang up Jonathan and Barbara and Nicky, and finally the Savoy Grill – this is only a forlorn hope – I never thought for a moment you'd be in.' Diana muttered something about being tired and having a matinée tomorrow, her voice sounded false and toneless. Martha went on. 'I don't want to be a bore, darling, but Helen and Jack have arrived from New York, and they're leaving on Saturday for Paris, and they've been trying all day to get seats for your show, and the nearest they could get was the fourteenth row, and I wondered if you could do anything about the house seats.' With a great effort Diana said: 'Of course, darling, I'll fix it with the box-office tomorrow.' 'You're an angel – here are Helen and Jack, they want to say "Hallo".' There was a slight pause, then Helen's husky Southern voice: 'Darling—'

Diana put her feet up and lay back on the bed, this was going to be a long business. She was in command of herself again, she had been a fool to imagine it was Jimmy, anyhow; he never telephoned unless she asked him to, that was one of the most maddening aspects of his good behaviour. Good behaviour to Jimmy was almost a religion. Excepting when they were alone together, he never for an instant betrayed by the flicker of an eyelash that they were anything more than casual acquaintances. There was no servility in his manner, no pandering to her stardom. On the contrary, the brief words he had occasion to speak to her in public were, if anything, a trifle brusque, perfectly polite, of course, but definitely without warmth. Helen's voice went on. She and Jack had had a terrible trip on the *Queen Mary*, and Jack had been sick as a dog for three whole days. Presently Jack came to the telephone and took up the conversation where Helen had left off. Diana lay still, giving a confident, assured performance, laughing gaily, dismissing her present success with just enough disarming professional modesty to be becoming. 'But, Jack dear, it's a marvellous part – nobody could go far wrong in a part like that. You wait until you see it – you'll see exactly what I mean. Not only that, but the cast's good too, Ronnie's superb. I think it's the best performance he's given since *The Lights Are Low*, and, of course, he's heaven to play with. He does a little bit of business with the breakfast tray at the beginning of the third act that's absolutely

162

magical. I won't tell you what it is, because it would spoil it for you, but just watch out for it – No dear, I can't have supper tomorrow night – I've a date with some drearies that I've already put off twice – no, really I couldn't again – how about lunch on Friday? You'd better come here and bring old Martha, too – all right – it's lovely to hear your voice again. The seats will be in your name in the box-office tomorrow night. Come backstage afterward, anyhow, even if you've hated it – goodbye!'

Diana put down the telephone and lit a cigarette, then she wrote on the pad by the bed: 'Remember fix house seats, Jack and Helen.' Next to the writing pad was a thermos jug of Ovaltine left for her by Dora. She looked at it irritably and then poured some out and sipped it.

Jimmy had probably gone straight home. He generally did. He wasn't a great one for going out, and didn't seem to have many friends except, of course, Elsie Lumley, who'd been in repertory with him, but that was all over now and she was safely married, or was she? Elsie Lumley, judging from what she knew of her, was the type that would be reluctant to let any old love die, married or not married. Elsie Lumley! Pretty, perhaps rather over vivacious, certainly talented. She'd be a star in a year or two if she behaved herself. The picture of Elsie and Jimmy together was unbearable – even though it all happened years ago – it *had* happened and had gone on for quite a long while, too. Elsie lying in his arms, pulling his head down to her mouth, running her fingers through his hair – Diana put down the cup of Ovaltine with a bang that spilt a lot of it into the saucer. She felt sick, as though something were dragging her heart down into her stomach. If Jimmy had gone straight home he'd be in his flat now, in bed probably, reading. There really wasn't any valid reason in the world why she shouldn't ring him up. If he didn't answer, he was out, and there was nothing else to do about it. If he was in, even if he had dropped off to sleep, he wouldn't really mind her just ringing up to say 'Good-night'.

She put out her hand to dial his number, then withdrew it again. It would be awful if someone else was there and answered the telephone, not that it was very likely, he only had a bed-sitting-room, but still he might have asked Bob Harley or Walter

Grayson home for a drink. If Walter Grayson heard her voice on the telephone it would be all over the theatre by tomorrow evening. He was one of those born theatrical gossips, amusing certainly, and quite a good actor, but definitely dangerous. She could, of course, disguise her voice. Just that twang of refined cockney that she had used in *The Short Year*. She put out her hand again, and again withdrew it. 'I'll have another cigarette and by the time I've smoked it, I shall decide whether to ring him up or not.' She hoisted herself up on the pillow and lit a cigarette, methodically and with pleasure. The ache had left her heart and she felt happier – unaccountably so, really; nothing had happened except the possibility of action, of lifting the receiver and dialling a number, of hearing his voice – rather sleepy, probably – saying: 'Hallo, who is it?' She puffed at her cigarette luxuriously watching the smoke curl up into the air. It was blue when it spiralled up from the end of the cigarette and grey when she blew it out of her mouth. It might, of course, irritate him being rung up, he might think she was being indiscreet or tiresome or even trying to check up on him: trying to find out whether he'd gone straight home, and whether he was alone or not.

How horrible if she rang up and he wasn't alone: if she heard his voice say, just as he was lifting the receiver: 'Don't move, darling, it's probably a wrong number,' something ordinary like that, so simple and so ordinary, implying everything, giving the whole game away. After all, he was young and good-looking, and they had neither of them vowed any vows of fidelity. It really wouldn't be so surprising if he indulged in a little fun on the side every now and then. Conducting a secret liaison with the star of the theatre in which you work must be a bit of a strain from time to time. A little undemanding, light, casual love with somebody else might be a relief.

Diana crushed out her cigarette angrily, her hands were shaking and she felt sick again. She swung her legs off the bed and, sitting on the edge of it, dialled his number viciously, as though she had found him out already; caught him red-handed. She listened to the ringing tone, it rang in twos – brrr-brrr – brrr-brrr. The telephone was next to his bed, that she knew, because once when she had dropped him home he had asked her in to see his hovel. It was a bed-sitting-room on the ground floor in one of those small, old-fashioned streets that run down to the river from John Street, Adelphi . . . brrr-brrr – brrr-brrr – she might have dialled the wrong number. She hung up and then redialled it, again the ringing tone, depressing and monotonous. He was out – he was out somewhere – but where could he possibly be? One more chance, she'd call the operator and ask her to give the number a special ring, just in case there had been a mistake.

The operator was most obliging, but after a few minutes her voice, detached and impersonal, announced that there was no reply from the number and that should she call again later? Diana said no, it didn't matter, she'd call in the morning. She replaced the receiver slowly, wearily, as though it were too heavy to hold any longer, then she buried her face in her hands.

Presently she got up again and began to walk up and down the room. The bed, rumpled where she had lain on it, but turned down, with her nightdress laid out, ready to get into, tortured her with the thought of the hours she would lie awake in it. Even Medinal, if she were stupid enough to take a couple of tablets before a matinée, wouldn't be any use tonight. That was what was so wonderful about being in love, it made you so happy! She laughed bitterly aloud and then caught herself laughing bitterly aloud and, just for a second, really laughed. Just a grain of humour left after all. She stopped in front of a long glass and addressed herself in a whisper, but with clear, precise enunciation as though she were trying to explain something to an idiot child. 'I don't care,' she said, 'I don't care if it's cheap or humiliating or unwise or undignified or mad, I'm going to do it, so there. I'm going to do it now, and if I have to wait all night in the street I shall see him, do you understand? I shall see him before I go to sleep, I don't mind if it's only for a moment, I shall see him. If the play closes tomorrow night. If I'm the scandal of London. If the stars fall out of the sky. If the world comes to an end! I shall see him before I go to sleep tonight. If he's alone or with somebody else. If he's drunk, sober or doped, I intend to see him. If he is in and his lights are out I shall bang on the window until I wake him and if, when I wake him, he's in bed with man, woman or child, I shall at least know. Beyond arguments and excuses I shall *know*. I don't care how foolish and neurotic I may appear to him. I don't care how high my position is, or how much I trail my pride in the dust. What's position anyway, and what's pride? To hell with them. I'm in love and I'm desperately unhappy. I know there's no reason to be unhappy, no cause for jealousy and that I should be ashamed of myself at my age, or at any age, for being so uncontrolled and for allowing this God-damned passion or obsession or whatever it is to conquer me, but there it is. It can't be helped. No more fighting – no more efforts to behave beautifully. I'm going to see him – I'm going now – and if he is unkind or angry and turns away from me I shall lie down in the gutter and howl.'

She picked up her hat from the sofa in the sitting-room, turned out all the lights, glanced in her bag to see if she had her keys all right and enough money for a taxi, and went out on to the landing, shutting the door furtively behind her. She debated for a moment whether to ring for the lift or slip down the stairs, finally deciding on the latter as it would be better on the whole if the lift-man didn't see her. He lived in the basement and there was little chance of him catching her unless by bad luck she happened to coincide with any of the other tenants coming in. She got out into the street unobserved and set off briskly in the direction of Orchard Street. It was a fine night, fortunately, but there had been rain earlier on and the roads were shining under the lights. She waited on the corner of Orchard Street and Portman Square for a taxi that came lolling toward her from the direction of Great Cumberland Place. She told the driver to stop just opposite the Little Theatre in John Street, Adelphi, and got in. The cab smelt musty and someone had been smoking a pipe in it. On the seat beside her something white caught her eye; she turned it over gingerly with her gloved hand, and discovered that it was a programme of her own play, with a large photograph of herself on the cover. She looked at the photograph critically. The cab was rattling along Oxford Street now, and the light was bright enough. The photograph had been taken a year ago in a Molyneux sports dress and small hat. It was a three-quarter length and she was sitting on the edge of a sofa, her profile half turned away from the camera. She looked young in it, although the poise of the head was assured, perhaps a trifle too assured.

She looked a little hard too, she thought, a little ruthless. She wondered if she was, really. If this journey she was making now, this unwise, neurotic excursion, merely boiled down to being an unregenerate determination to get what she wanted, when she wanted it, at no matter what price. She thought it over calmly, this business of being determined. After all, it was largely that, plus undoubted talent and personality, that got her where she was today. She wondered if she were popular in the theatre. She knew the stagehands liked her, of course, they were easy; just remembering to say 'thank you' when any of them held open a door for her or 'good-evening' when she passed them on the stage was enough – they were certainly easy because their manners were good, and so were hers; but the rest of the company – not Ronnie, naturally, he was in more or less the same position as herself; the others, little Cynthia French, for instance, the *ingénue*, did she hate her bitterly in secret? Did she envy her and wish her to fail? Was all that wide-eyed, faintly servile eagerness to please, merely masking an implacable ambition, a sweet, strong, female loathing? She thought not on the whole, Cynthia was far too timid a creature, unless, of course, she was a considerably finer actress off the stage than she was on. Walter Grayson, she knew, liked her all right. She'd known him for years, they'd been in several plays together. Lottie Carnegie was certainly waspish at moments, but only with that innate defensiveness of an elderly actress who hadn't quite achieved what she originally set out to achieve. There were several of them about, old-timers without any longer much hope left of becoming stars, but with enough successful work behind them to assure their getting good character parts. They all had their little mannerisms and peculiarities and private fortresses of pride. Lottie was all right really, in fact as far as she, Diana, was concerned she was all sweetness and light, but, of course, that might be because she hated Ronnie. Once, years ago apparently, he had been instrumental in having her turned down for a part for which he considered her unsuitable. The others liked her well enough, she thought, at least she hoped they did; it was horrid not to be liked; but she hadn't any illusions as to what would happen if she made a false step. This affair with Jimmy, for example. If that became known in the theatre the whole of London would be buzzing with it. She winced at the thought. That would be horrible. Once more, by the light of a street lamp at the bottom of the Haymarket, she looked at the photograph. She wondered if she had looked like that to the man with the pipe to whom the programme had belonged; whether he had taken his wife with him or his mistress; whether they'd liked the play and cried dutifully in the last act, or been bored and disappointed and wished they'd gone to a musical comedy. How surprised they'd be if they knew that the next person to step into the taxi after they'd left it was Diana Reed, Diana Reed herself, the same woman they had so recently been applauding, as she bowed and smiled at them in that shimmering silver evening gown – that reminded her to tell Dora at the matinée tomorrow that the paillettes where her cloak fastened were getting tarnished and that she must either ring up the shop or see if Mrs Blake could deal with it in the wardrobe.

The taxi drew up with a jerk opposite to the Little Theatre. Diana got out and paid the driver. He said: 'Good-night, miss,' and drove away down the hill, leaving her on the edge of the kerb feeling rather dazed, almost forgetting what she was there for. The urgency that had propelled her out of her flat and into that taxi seemed to have evaporated somewhere between Oxford Street and here. Perhaps it was the photograph on the programme, the reminder of herself as others saw her, as she should be, poised and well-dressed with head held high, not in contempt, nothing supercilious about it, but secure and dignified, above the arena. Those people who had taken that taxi, who had been to the play – how shocked they'd be if they could see her now, not just standing alone in a dark street, that wouldn't of course shock them particularly, merely surprise them; but if they could know, by some horrid clairvoyance, why she was there. If, just for an instant, they could see into her mind. Diana Reed, that smooth, gracious creature whose stage loves and joys and sorrows they had so often enjoyed, furtively loitering about in the middle of the night in the hopes of spending a few minutes with a comparatively insignificant young man whom she liked going to bed with. Diana resolutely turned in the opposite direction from Jimmy's street and walked round by the side of the Tivoli into the Strand. Surely it was a little more than that? Surely she was being unnecessarily hard on herself. There was a sweetness about Jimmy, a quality, apart from his damned sex appeal. To begin with, he was well-bred, a gentleman. (What a weak, nauseating alibi, as though that could possibly matter one way or another and yet, of course, it did.) His very gentleness, his strict code of behaviour. His fear, so much stronger even than hers, that anyone should discover their secret. Also he was intelligent, infinitely more knowledgeable and better read than she. All that surely made a difference, surely justified her behaviour a little bit? She walked along the Strand toward Fleet Street, as though she were hurrying to keep an important appointment. There were still a lot of people about and on the other side of the street two drunken men were happily staggering along with their arms round each other's necks, singing 'Ramona'. Suddenly to her horror she saw Violet Cassel and Donald Ross approaching her, they had obviously been supping at the Savoy and decided to walk a little before taking a cab. With an instinctive gesture she jammed her hat down over her eyes and darted into Heppell's so quickly that she collided with a woman who was just coming out and nearly knocked her down. The woman said, 'Christ, a fugitive from a chain gang?' and waving aside Diana's apologies, went unsteadily into the street. Diana, faced with the enquiring stare of the man behind the counter and slightly unhinged by her encounter in the doorway, and the fact that Donald and Violet were at that moment passing the shop, racked her brains for something to buy. Her eyes lighted on a bottle of emerald green liquid labelled 'Ess Viotto for the hands'. 'I should like that,' she said, pointing to it. The man, without looking at her again, wrapped it up and handed it to her. She paid for it and went out of the shop. Violet and Donald were crossing over further down. She walked slowly back the way she had come. An empty taxi cruising along close to the kerb passed her and almost stopped. She hailed it, gave the driver her address, got in and sank thankfully back on to the seat. 'A fugitive from a chain gang.' She smiled and closed her eyes for a moment. 'What an escape!' She felt utterly exhausted as if she had passed through a tremendous

169

crisis, she was safe, safe as houses, safe from herself and humiliation and indignity. No more of such foolishness. She wondered whether or not she had replaced the stopper in the thermos. She hoped she had, because the prospect of sitting up, snug in bed, with a mind at peace and a cup of Ovaltine seemed heavenly. She opened her eyes as the taxi was turning into Lower Regent Street and looked out of the window. A man in a camel's-hair coat and a soft brown hat was waiting on the corner to cross the road. Jimmy! She leant forward hurriedly and tried to slide the glass window back in order to tell the driver to stop, but it wouldn't budge. She rapped on the glass violently. The driver looked round in surprise and drew into the kerb. She was out on the pavement in a second, fumbling in her bag. 'I've forgotten something,' she said breathlessly. 'Here' – she gave him a half a crown and turned and ran toward Jimmy. He had crossed over by now and was just turning into Cockspur Street. She had to wait a moment before crossing because two cars came by and then a bus. When she got round the corner she could still see him just passing the lower entrance to the Carlton. She put on a great spurt and caught up with him just as he was about to cross the Haymarket. He turned his head slightly just as she was about to clutch at his sleeve. He was a pleasant-looking young man with fair hair and a little moustache. Diana stopped dead in her tracks and watched him cross the road, a stream of traffic went by and he was lost to view. She stood there trying to get her breath and controlling an overpowering desire to burst into tears. She stamped her foot hard as though by so doing she could crush her agonising, bitter disappointment into the ground.

A passing policeman looked at her suspiciously, so she moved miserably across the road and walked on toward Trafalgar Square, past the windows of the shipping agencies filled with smooth models of ocean liners. She stopped at one of them for a moment and rested her forehead against the cold glass, staring at a white steamer with two yellow funnels; its decks meticulously scrubbed and its paintwork shining in the light from the street lamps. Then, pulling herself together, she set off firmly in the direction of the Adelphi. No use dithering about any more. She had, in leaving the flat in the first place, obeyed an irresistible but perfectly understandable impulse to see Jimmy. Since then, she had hesitated and vacillated and tormented herself into a state bordering on hysteria. No more of that, it was stupid, worse than stupid, this nerve-racking conflict between reason and emotion was insane. Reason had done its best and failed. No reason in the world could now woo her into going back to that empty flat without seeing Jimmy. If Fate hadn't dressed that idiotic young man with a moustache in Jimmy's camel's-hair coat and Jimmy's hat, all would have been well. If Fate had arbitrarily decided, as it apparently had, that she was to make a fool of herself, then make a fool of herself she would. Jimmy was probably fast asleep by now and would be furious at being awakened. She was, very possibly, by this lamentable, silly behaviour, about to wreck something precious, something which, in future years, she might have been able to look back upon with a certain wistful nostalgia. Now of course, after she had observed Jimmy's irritation and thinly-veiled disgust, after he had kissed her and comforted her and packed her off home in a taxi, she would have to face one fact clearly and bravely and that fact would be that a love affair, just another love affair, was ended. Not a violent break or a quarrel or anything like that, just a gentle, painful decline, something to be glossed over and forgotten. By the time she had reached the top of Jimmy's street there were tears in her eyes.

She walked along the pavement on tiptoe. His windows were dark, she peered into them over the area railings. His curtains were not drawn, his room was empty. She walked over the road to where there was a street lamp and looked at her wristwatch. Ten past two. She stood there leaning against a railing, not far from the lamp, for several minutes. There were no lights in any of the houses except one on the corner. On the top floor, a little square of yellow blind with a shadow occasionally moving behind it. On her left, beyond the end of the road which was a cul-de-sac, were the trees of the gardens along the Embankment; they rustled slightly in the damp breeze. Now and then she heard the noise of a train rumbling hollowly over Charing Cross bridge, and occasionally the mournful hoot of a tug on the river. Where on earth could he be at this hour of the morning? He hated going out, or at least so he always said. He didn't drink much either. He wouldn't be sitting up with a lot of cronies just drinking. He was very responsible about his job too and in addition to a matinée tomorrow there was an understudy rehearsal at eleven – she knew that because she had happened to notice it on the board. He couldn't have gone home to his parents; they lived on the Isle of Wight. She sauntered slowly up to the corner of John Street and looked up and down it. No taxi in sight, nothing, only a cat stalking along by the railings. She stooped down and said 'Puss, puss' to it but it ignored her and disappeared down some steps. Suddenly a taxi turned into the lower end of the street. Diana took to her heels and ran. Supposing it were Jimmy coming home with somebody – supposing he looked out and saw her standing on the pavement, watching him. Panic seized her. On the left, on the opposite side of the road from the house where he lived, was a dark archway. She dived into it and pressed herself flat against the wall. The taxi turned into the street and drew up. She peeped round the corner and saw a fat man and woman in evening dress get out of it and let themselves into one of the houses. When the taxi had backed and driven away she emerged from the archway. 'I'll walk,' she said to herself out loud. 'I'll walk up and down this street twenty times and if he hasn't come by then I'll – I'll walk up and down it another twenty times.' She started walking and laughing at herself at the same time, quite genuine laughter; she listened to it and it didn't sound in the least hysterical. I'm feeling better, she thought, none of it matters nearly as much as I think it does, I've been making mountains out of molehills. I'm enjoying this really, it's an adventure. There's something strange and exciting in being out alone in the city at dead of night, I must do it more often. She laughed again at the picture of herself solemnly setting out two or three times a week on solitary nocturnal jaunts. After about the fifteenth time she had turned and retraced her steps she met Jimmy face-to-face at the corner. He stopped in amazement and said, 'My God – Diana – what on earth—'

She held out to him the parcel she'd been holding.

'I've brought you a present,' she said with a little giggle. 'It's Ess Viotto – for the hands!'

Stop Me if You've Heard It

'Please God,' she whispered to herself. 'Don't let it be the one about the Englishman and the Scotsman and the American in the railway carriage, nor the one about the old lady and the parrot, nor the one about the couple arriving at the seaside hotel on their honeymoon night! I'll settle for any of the others, but please, please merciful God, not one of those three – I can't bear it. If it's one of those three, particularly the Englishman and the Scotsman and the American in the railway carriage, I shall go mad – I shall do something awful – I'll shriek – I'll make a hideous scene – I'll bash his head in with a bottle—'

Her husband, sitting opposite to her at the table, cleared his throat. Her whole body became rigid at the sound. With a great effort she took a cigarette out of a little blue enamel pot in front of her and lit it. Some of the general conversation at the table died away into polite attentiveness. She was aware, wretchedly aware, of the quick, resigned glance that Louis Bennet exchanged with Susan Lake. She looked at her host, Carroll Davis, leaning forward politely, his good-looking face blank. Carroll was kind; Carroll understood; his manners were dictated by his heart – he wouldn't hurt Budge's feelings for the world; he would listen appreciatively and laugh at the right moments, saving his loudest, most convincing laugh for the point at the end, and Budge would never know, never remotely suspect for an instant, that he hadn't been amused.

The others would laugh too, of course, but there would be an undertone of malice – their alert, cruel minds would be silently communicating with one another. 'Poor Budge,' they would be saying, 'the kiss of death on every party – he never knows when to stop. In the old days he used to be funny on the stage, but now he's even lost that. Why does Carroll ask him? Obviously, for Marty's sake – she *must* know how awful he is. She *must* realise, deep down, that she's married to the most monumental cracking bore. Why doesn't she leave him? Why doesn't she at least come to parties without him? She knows we're all old friends – she knows we love her. Why the hell doesn't she leave that aggressive, over-eager little megalomaniac at home?'

Marty drew deeply at her cigarette. Jane and Shirley and Bobby Peek were still talking and laughing at the other end of the table. They had not noticed – yet. They were still unaware of doom. Budge shot them a quick, resentful look and cleared his throat again. They glanced up, and the light went out of their faces. Shirley stabbed out her cigarette, put her head back and closed her eyes. Marty felt an insane desire to lean forward and slap her face violently. 'Listen, you languid, supercilious bitch, Budge Ripley's going to tell a story. Sit up and listen, and mind your manners! He was telling stories – amusing people – millions of people – making them laugh until they cried, making them forget their troubles – making them happy – before you were born. All right, all right – he may be a bore now – he may have lost his touch, but mind your manners – lean forward, look interested, whatever you feel – bitch – spoiled, supercilious bitch.'

'Stop me if you've heard it.' Budge's voice grated in the silence. He caught her eye, and, painting an encouraging smile on her face, she leaned forward. No more than a split second could have passed before he began, but in that split second the years of her life with him rolled out before her – jerkily and confused in memory, like a panorama she had been taken to see at Earl's Court when she was a child.

She had been getting on quite well twenty years ago when she had first met him – chorus and understudy and small parts here and there. She had never been pretty, but there was something about her that people liked, a comic quality of personality. Carroll had always asked her to his grandest parties regardless of the fact that she was really small fry in the theatre compared with his other guests. She had had wit always, a realistic, unaffected cockney humour, quick as a whip but without malice. It was at one of Carroll's parties, in this same house, that Budge had first noticed her. It was in this same house three years later, after she had slept with him hundreds of times, that he had told her that his divorce was through and that they could get married. Seventeen years ago that was. They had moved into Number 18 – she had been so proud, so grateful, and he had been so sweet. No more stage work for her, no more prancing on and off for finales and opening choruses. She ran the house fairly well, went to all Budge's first nights in a box or stalls; stood with him afterward in the dressing-room while people came rushing in to say how marvellous he was. 'Funnier than ever.' 'I laughed till I was sick.' 'Nobody like you, Budge, the comic genius of the age – your inventiveness – your pathos too – only really great comedians have that particular quality, that subtle balance between grave and gay—'

They gave parties at Number 18 – gay and amusing, lasting sometimes until dawn. Several years of happiness passed – several years of excitement and success and occasional holidays in the South of France. Then, insidiously, the rot began to set in – very gradually at first, so gradually, indeed, that it was a long time before she even suspected it. A strange rot, composed of circumstances, small, psychological maladjustments, mutual irritations, sudden outbursts of temper; the subtle cause of it all still obscure, still buried deep.

It was about then that he began to be unfaithful to her – nothing serious – just an occasional roll in the hay with someone who took his fancy. Marty found out about this almost immediately, and it hurt her immeasurably. She reasoned with herself, of course; she exerted every ounce of common sense and self-control, and succeeded bleakly insofar that she said nothing and did nothing, but from then on everything was different. There was no security any more, and no peace of mind. It was not that she cared so desperately about him popping into bed every now and then with someone else – only a fool, married happily for years to a famous star, would make a fuss about that. It was something deeper, something that bewildered and gnawed at her, something more important that she knew to exist but somehow could not identify.

It was later – quite a long while later – that the truth suddenly became clear to her, that the answer to this riddle, which had tortured her for so long, suddenly flashed into her consciousness with all the blatant clarity of a neon light – a neon light sign flashing on and off with hideous monotony one vulgar, piteous word, jealousy. Budge was jealous of her. He was jealous of her wit, her gaiety, her friends. She could have slept with other men as much as she liked, and he would have forgiven her; she could have drunk herself into a coma every night, and he would have been loving and concerned and understanding; but because she was herself, because people of all kinds found her good company, because she could, without effort, embroider an ordinary anecdote with genuine humour and infectious gaiety and be loved and welcomed for it – this he could never forgive; for this, she realised in that blinding flash of revelation, he would hate her until the day he died.

'Stop me if you've heard it!' That idiotic, insincere phrase – that false, unconvincing opening gambit – as though people ever had the courage to stop anyone however many times they'd heard it! Human beings could be brave – incredibly brave about many things. They could fly in jet-propelled planes; fling themselves from the sky in parachutes; hurl themselves fully clothed into turbulent seas to rescue drowning children; crawl on their mortal stomachs through bullet-spattered mud and take pins out of unexploded bombs or shells or whatever they were, but no one, no one in the whole twisting, agonised world was brave enough to say loudly and clearly, 'Yes, I have heard it. It is dull and unfunny; it bores the liver and lights out of me. I have heard it over and over again, and if I have to hear it once more in any of the years that lie between me and the grave, I'll plunge a fork into your silly throat – I'll pull out your clacking tongue with my nails.'

Marty suddenly caught sight of her hands. One was resting on the table; the other was holding her cigarette; both were trembling. She looked miserably round the table. They were all listening with exaggerated courtesy. Shirley was looking down, her long scarlet-tipped fingers scratching about among the breadcrumbs by her plate, making them into little patterns, a circle with one larger one in the middle, then a triangle. Budge's voice grated on. The Englishman, the Scotsman and the American, 'I say you know,' 'Och aye,' 'Gee.' Marty stared across the years at his face. There it was, aged a little, but not much changed since she had loved it so; the same kindly, rather protuberant blue eyes, the fleshy nose, the straw-coloured hair, the wide comedian's mouth. His head was bent forward eagerly. He was talking a trifle too quickly because somewhere writhing deep within him was a suspicion that his audience was not wholly with him, he hadn't quite got them. He finished the Scotsman's bit. Bobby Peek laughed, and Marty could have flung her arms round his neck and hugged him for it.

Budge's eyes shone with pleasure – 'Gee, Buddy!' There was quite a loud laugh at the end of the story.

Carroll's kindness triumphed over his wisdom. 'That was wonderful, Budge,' he said. 'Nobody can tell a story like you!'

Marty's heart died in her. She made a swift, instinctive movement to get up from the table. Budge looked at her, and his eyes hardened. She sat still as death, chained to her chair. He cleared his throat again.

'Marty half getting up like that reminded me of a good one,' he said. 'Do you know the one about the shy lady at the dinner party who wanted to go to the telephone?'

There was a polite murmur round the table. Shirley took her compact out of her bag and scrutinised her face in the little mirror. Louis Bennet coughed and exchanged another meaning glance with Susan. Budge pushed back his chair, recrossed his legs and started . . .

Marty stared down into her lap. There was some gold embroidery on her dress and it seemed to be expanding and changing into curious shapes because her eyes were filled with tears.

A hundred years later they were driving home. It was very late and the streets were almost empty. Budge was bunched up in his corner, sulky and silent. Marty stared at the back of Gordon's neck. Gordon drove well, but he was inclined to take risks. As a rule she was nervous and made him go slowly, but tonight she didn't care; she wouldn't have minded if he had driven at sixty miles an hour, careering along Oxford Street, crashing all the lights.

They arrived at Number 18 still in silence. Budge said goodnight to Gordon, and they went into the house. Rose had left the drink-tray on the dining-room table and a plate of curly-looking sandwiches.

Budge poured himself out a whisky and soda. 'I'm going on up,' he said. 'I'm tired.'

Suddenly something seemed to crack inside Marty's head and

she started to laugh. There was an ugly note in the laugh which she recognised, but she had neither the strength nor the will to do anything about it.

'You must be,' she said. 'Oh, my God, you certainly must be!'

Budge stopped at the door and turned and looked at her.

'And what exactly do you mean by that?' he asked.

'Don't you know?' she said, and her voice sounded shrill and hysterical. 'Don't you really know? Haven't you got the faintest idea?'

Budge's already red face flushed, and he advanced two steps toward her. 'What's the matter with you?'

Marty backed away from him, still laughing miserably.

'This is a good one,' she said. 'Stop me if you've heard it. Stop me if you've heard it or not, because if you don't you'll never forgive me and I shall never forgive myself.'

Budge frowned. 'Are you drunk?'

Marty shook her head dumbly. She felt the tears starting and tried to wipe them away with the back of her hand. Budge came closer to her and looked carefully into her face. There was no more anger in his eyes, only bewilderment. She tried to look away, to escape from that puzzled, anxious face. She backed farther and, feeling the edge of a chair under her knees, sank down into it.

'What's the matter?' Budge persisted. 'You're not ill or anything, are you? Is it anything to do with me? What have I done?'

He put his hand on her arm. She felt the warmth of it through her sleeve. Suddenly her hysteria evaporated. She felt utterly exhausted, but no longer wild, no longer shrill and nerve-strained and cruel. She put her hand up, and pressed his more firmly on to her arm. Then she gave a little giggle, not a very convincing one really, but good enough.

'You may well ask what you've done,' she said. 'You may well ask if it's anything to do with you—'

Her voice broke, and, bringing her face against his stomach, she started crying thoroughly and satisfyingly.

Budge remained silent, but his other hand smoothed her hair away from her forehead. After a moment or two she controlled herself a bit and pushed him gently away.

'You've given me a miserable evening,' she said huskily. 'You never took your eyes off Shirley Dale from the beginning of supper to the end. You then behave like a sulky little boy all the way home in the car, and, to round the whole thing off, you help yourself to a drink without even asking if I want one and tell me you're tired! You're an inconsiderate, lecherous little pig and I can't imagine why I ever let you lead me to the Registry Office.'

She rose to her feet and put her arms round him tightly. She felt his body relax.

He gave a complacent chuckle. 'Of all the bloody fools,' he said. The warmth was back in his voice, the crisis had passed and the truth was stamped down again deep into the ground.

He led her over to the table and mixed her a drink. 'Shirley Dale, indeed – you must be out of your mind!'

She stood there with one arm still around him, sipping her drink. Nothing more was said until he had switched off the lights and they had gone upstairs. They talked ordinarily while they undressed; the familiarity of the bedroom seemed over-eager to put their hearts at ease.

Later on, after he had attacked his teeth in the bathroom with his customary violence, sprinkled himself with Floris 127 and put on his pyjamas, he came over and sat on the edge of her bed.

She smiled and reached out and patted his hand. Then gently, almost timidly, as though she were not quite sure of her ground, she pulled him toward her. 'I've got something to tell you,' she said. 'Stop me if you've heard it.'

The temperature and tempo of millions of lives rose and increased in August 1939, but for me the pre-war past died on the day when Mr Neville Chamberlain returned with such gay insouciance from Munich in 1938.

Keen to see for himself what was happening in Europe, Coward spent the spring and summer of 1939 travelling abroad. His trip began in Warsaw, and took him to Russia, where he stayed at the Astoria Hotel in Leningrad.

The dining-room was cool and dim and the tablecloths were filthy. I asked for caviare, which was not on the menu, and got it, doubtless because Vox, having arbitrarily taken my situation in hand, were determined that I should have no cause for criticism. I was glad of this, because it was large and grey and delicious. The chicken that followed it was also large and grey, but less delicious. The waiters who served it were small and grey, and their suits, which had originally set out to be white, were very grey indeed and looked as though they had been slept in. A string orchestra, with a heartless disregard for proletarian feelings, played a selection from *The Dollar Princess*.

From Russia he travelled to Finland where he paid a memorable visit to the composer Sibelius.

During my stay in Helsinki someone suggested that I should pay a call on Sibelius, who, although he lived a life of the utmost quiet and seclusion, would, I was assured, be more than delighted to receive me. This, later, proved to be an overstatement. However, encouraged by the mental picture of the great Master being practically unable to contain himself at the thought of meeting face to face the man who had composed 'A Room with a View' and 'Mad Dogs and Englishmen', I drove out graciously to call upon him. His house was a few miles away in the country and my guide-interpreter and I arrived there about noon. We were received by a startled, bald-headed gentleman whom I took to be an aged family retainer. He led us, without any marked signs of enthusiasm, on to a small, trellis-enclosed verandah, and left us alone. We conversed in low, reverent voices and offered each other cigarettes and waited with rising nervous tension for the Master to appear. I remembered regretting bitterly my casual approach to classical music and trying frantically in my mind to disentangle the works of Sibelius from those of Delius. After about a quarter of an hour the bald-headed man reappeared carrying a tray upon which was a decanter of wine and a plate of biscuits. He put this on the table and then, to my surprise, sat down and looked at us. The silence became almost unbearable, and my friend muttered something in Finnish to which the bald-headed gentleman replied with an exasperated nod. It then dawned upon me that this was the great man himself, and furthermore that he hadn't the faintest idea who I was, who my escort was, or what we were doing there at all. Feeling embarrassed and extremely silly I smiled vacuously and offered him a cigarette, which he refused. My friend then rose, I thought a trifle officiously, and poured out three glasses of wine. We then proceeded to toast each other politely but in the same oppressive silence. I asked my friend if Mr Sibelius could speak English or French and he said 'No'. I then asked him to explain to him how very much I admired his music and what an honour it was for me to meet him personally. This was translated, upon which Sibelius rose abruptly to his feet and offered me a biscuit. I accepted it with rather overdone gratitude, and then down came the silence again, and I looked forlornly past Sibelius's head through a gap in the trellis at the road. Finally, realising that unless I did something decisive we should probably stay there until sundown, I got up and asked my friend – whom I could willingly have garrotted – to thank Mr Sibelius for receiving me and to explain once again how honoured I was to meet him, and that I hoped he would forgive us for leaving so soon but we had an appointment at the hotel for lunch. Upon this being communicated to him, Sibelius smiled for the first time and we shook hands with enthusiasm. He escorted us to the gate and waved happily as we drove away.

My friend, whose name I am not withholding for any secret reasons but merely because I cannot remember it, seemed oblivious of the fact that the interview had not been a glittering success. Perhaps, being a rising journalist, he had already achieved immunity to the subtler nuances of social embarrassment. At all events he dismissed my reproaches quite airily. Mr Sibelius, he said, was well known to be both shy and unapproachable. I replied bitterly that in that case it had been most inconsiderate to all parties concerned to have arranged the interview in the first place, for although I was neither shy nor unapproachable, I was acutely sensitive to atmosphere and resented being placed in a false position possibly as much as Mr Sibelius did. We wrangled on in this strain until we reached the hotel, where we parted with a certain frigidity. Later, troubled by conscience, I wrote a brief note of apology to Sibelius, who, despite the fact that his seclusion had been invaded and the peace of his morning disrupted, had at least received me with courtesy and given me a biscuit.

By August Coward had two plays in rehearsal, This Happy Breed *and* Present Laughter, *but the invasion of Poland, on 1 September 1939, put paid to the planned openings. He spent the first months of the war working in Paris for the Ministry of Information, a posting which suited him but a job that did not. He was then sent on a propaganda mission to the United States but, at the time of the fall of France, he pulled every string he could to get home.*

I did love England and all it stood for. I loved its follies and apathies and curious streaks of genius; I loved standing to attention for 'God Save the King'; I loved British courage, British humour, and British understatement; I loved the justice, efficiency and even the dullness of British Colonial Administration. I loved the people – the ordinary, the extraordinary, the good, the bad, the indifferent, and what is more I belonged to that exasperating, weather-sodden little island with its uninspired cooking, its muddled thinking and its unregenerate pride, and it belonged to me whether it liked it or not. There was no escape, no getting round it, that was my personal truth and in facing up to it, once and for all, I experienced a strong relief.

A year or so later those personal feelings became the basis of a song about the battered capital of the free world.

London Pride

Verse 1

London Pride has been handed down to us.
London Pride is a flower that's free.
London Pride means our own dear town to us,
And our pride it for ever will be.
Woa, Liza,
See the coster barrows,
Vegetable marrows
And the fruit piled high.
Woa, Liza,
Little London sparrows,
Covent Garden Market where the costers cry.
Cockney feet
Mark the beat of history.
Every street
Pins a memory down.
Nothing ever can quite replace
The grace of London Town.

Interlude

There's a little city flower every spring unfailing
Growing in the crevices by some London railing,
Though it has a Latin name, in town and countryside
We in England call it London Pride.

Verse 2

London Pride has been handed down to us.
London Pride is a flower that's free.
London Pride means our own dear town to us,
And our pride it for ever will be.
Hey, lady,
When the day is dawning

See the policeman yawning
On his lonely beat.
Gay lady,
Mayfair in the morning,
Hear your footsteps echo in the empty street.
Early rain
And the pavement's glistening.
All Park Lane
In a shimmering gown.
Nothing ever could break or harm
The charm of London Town.

Interlude

In our city darkened now, street and square and crescent,
We can feel our living past in our shadowed present,
Ghosts beside our starlit Thames
Who lived and loved and died
Keep throughout the ages London Pride.

Verse 3

London Pride has been handed down to us.
London Pride is a flower that's free.
London Pride means our own dear town to us,
And our pride it for ever will be.
Grey city
Stubbornly implanted,
Taken so for granted
For a thousand years.
Stay, city,
Smokily enchanted,
Cradle of our memories and hopes and fears.
Every Blitz
Your resistance
Toughening,
From the Ritz
To the Anchor and Crown,
Nothing ever could override
The pride of London Town.

Coward was reluctant to accept that his most valuable war work would be as an entertainer. Churchill's advice, 'Go and sing for them when the guns are firing–that's your job!' seemed to him absurd. Eventually he did just that, but first came a play and a film which, in their different ways, were his main contributions to the nation's morale.

Between 9 May, when *Blithe Spirit* was finished at Port Meirion, and 16 June, when it opened its preliminary tour in Manchester, several things happened. Rudolf Hess arrived in Scotland, which affected me very little, although it flung the Press boys at the Savoy into a frenzy of excitement and wild surmise. The Metro-Goldwyn-Mayer epic film of *Bitter Sweet* in violent Technicolor arrived at the Empire, which affected me even less, for I had already seen it in a projection room in Hollywood and had decided, sensibly, to wipe it from my mind. It was directed with gusto by Mr Victor Saville and sung with even more gusto by Miss Jeanette Macdonald and Mr Nelson Eddy. It was vulgar, lacking in taste and bore little relation to my original story. What did affect me, however, was the news on 27th May of the sinking of H M S *Kelly*, although naturally I had no idea at the time how much more this was destined to affect me in the future. Immediately the news broke I telephoned to Robert Neville at the Admiralty, and he told me that Mountbatten had survived and was coming home. This was a great relief, but knowing how much his ship meant to him, and remembering with what pride he had taken me over her only a short while ago, I felt miserable.

Blithe Spirit, after the usual casting troubles and complications, duly opened in Manchester and was an enormous success. The London opening night was on 2 July at the Piccadilly Theatre, and a very curious opening night it was. The audience, socially impeccable from the journalistic point of view and mostly in uniform, had to walk across planks laid over the rubble caused by a recent air raid to see a light comedy about death. They enjoyed it, I am glad to say, and it ran from that sunny summer evening through the remainder of the war and out the other side. A year later it transferred to the St James's Theatre for a while, and then finally went to the Duchess, where at last it closed on 9 March 1946.

Blithe Spirit *begins on a fine summer evening when Charles Con-domine and his second wife, Ruth, have invited their neighbours the Bradmans to dine. In a spirit of light-hearted enquiry they ask the third guest, the eccentric Madame Arcati, to conduct a seance for them. It appears to be a complete failure but, when it is over, Charles is appalled to find that his first wife, Elvira, has come back from the dead. His confusion is further confounded by the fact that only he can see or hear her.*

BLITHE SPIRIT

Act II

It is about nine-thirty the next morning. The sun is pouring in through the open french windows.

    Breakfast table set Left centre below piano. RUTH *sitting left of table back to window reading* The Times. CHARLES *comes in and crosses to window – he kisses her.*

CHARLES: Good-morning, darling.

RUTH [*with a certain stiffness*]: Good-morning, Charles.

CHARLES [*going to the open window and taking a deep breath*]: It certainly is.

RUTH: What certainly is what?

CHARLES: A good morning – a tremendously good morning – there isn't a cloud in the sky and everything looks newly washed.

RUTH [*turning a page of* The Times]: Edith's keeping your breakfast hot – you'd better ring.

CHARLES [*crosses to mantelpiece and rings bell up stage*]: Anything interesting in *The Times?*

RUTH: Don't be silly, Charles.

CHARLES [*sitting at the table and pouring himself out some coffee*]: I intend to work all day.

RUTH: Good.

CHARLES [*comes back to breakfast table*]: It's extraordinary about daylight, isn't it?

RUTH: How do you mean?

CHARLES: The way it reduces everything to normal.

RUTH: Does it?

CHARLES [*sits right of table opposite* RUTH *– firmly*]: Yes – it does.

RUTH: I'm sure I'm very glad to hear it.

187

CHARLES: You're very glacial this morning.

RUTH: Are you surprised?

CHARLES: Frankly – yes. I expected more of you.

RUTH: Well, really!

CHARLES: I've always looked upon you as a woman of perception and understanding.

RUTH: Perhaps this is one of my off days.

[EDITH *comes in with some bacon and eggs and toast – comes to above table between* CHARLES *and* RUTH.]

CHARLES [*cheerfully*]: Good-morning, Edith.

EDITH: Good-morning, sir.

CHARLES: Feeling fit?

EDITH: Yes, sir – thank you, sir.

CHARLES: How's cook?

EDITH: I don't know, sir – I haven't asked her.

CHARLES: You should. You should begin every day by asking everyone how they are – it oils the wheels.

EDITH: Yes, sir.

CHARLES: Greet her from me, will you?

EDITH: Yes, sir.

RUTH: That will be all for the moment, Edith.

EDITH: Yes'm.   [EDITH *goes out.*

RUTH: I wish you wouldn't be facetious with the servants, Charles – it confuses them and undermines their morale.

CHARLES: I consider that point of view retrogressive, if not downright feudal.

RUTH: I don't care what you consider it, I have to run the house and you don't.

CHARLES: Are you implying that I couldn't?

RUTH: You're at liberty to try.

CHARLES: I take back what I said about it being a good morning – it's a horrid morning.

RUTH: You'd better eat your breakfast while it's hot.

CHARLES: It isn't.

RUTH [*putting down* The Times]: Now look here, Charles – in your younger days this display of roguish flippancy might have been alluring – in a middle-aged novelist it's nauseating.

CHARLES: Would you like me to writhe at your feet in a frenzy of self-abasement?

RUTH: That would be equally nauseating but certainly more appropriate.

CHARLES: I really don't see what I've done that's so awful.

RUTH: You behaved abominably last night. You wounded me and insulted me.

CHARLES: I was the victim of an aberration.

RUTH: Nonsense – you were drunk.

CHARLES: Drunk?

RUTH: You had four strong dry martinis before dinner – a great deal too much burgundy at dinner – heaven knows how much port and kümmel with Dr Bradman while I was doing my best to entertain that mad woman – and then two double brandies later – I gave them to you myself – of course you were drunk.

CHARLES: So that's your story, is it?

RUTH: You refused to come to bed and finally when I came down at three in the morning to see what had happened to you, I found you in an alcoholic coma on the sofa with the fire out and your hair all over your face.

CHARLES: I was not in the least drunk, Ruth. Something happened to me last night – something very peculiar happened to me.

RUTH: Nonsense.

CHARLES: It isn't nonsense – I know it looks like nonsense now in the clear remorseless light of day, but last night it was far from being nonsense – I honestly had some sort of hallucination . . .

RUTH: I would really rather not discuss it any further.

CHARLES: But you must discuss it – it's very disturbing.

RUTH: There I agree with you. It showed you up in a most unpleasant light – I find that extremely disturbing.

CHARLES: I swear to you that during the seance I was convinced that I heard Elvira's voice—

RUTH: Nobody else did.

CHARLES: I can't help that – I did.

RUTH: You couldn't have.

CHARLES: And later on I was equally convinced that she was in this room – I saw her distinctly and talked to her. After you'd gone up to bed we had quite a cosy little chat.

RUTH: And you seriously expect me to believe that you weren't drunk?

CHARLES: I *know* I wasn't drunk. If I'd been all that drunk I should have a dreadful hangover now, shouldn't I?

RUTH: I'm not at all sure that you haven't.

CHARLES: I haven't got a trace of a headache – my tongue's not coated – look at it— [*He puts out his tongue.*]

RUTH: I've not the least desire to look at your tongue, kindly put it in again.

CHARLES [*rises, crosses to mantelpiece and lights cigarette*]: I know what it is – you're frightened.

RUTH: Frightened! Rubbish. What is there to be frightened of?

CHARLES: Elvira. You wouldn't have minded all that much even if I had been drunk – it's only because it was all mixed up with Elvira.

RUTH: I seem to remember last night before dinner telling you that your views of female psychology were rather didactic. I was right. I should have added that they were puerile.

CHARLES: That was when it all began.

RUTH: When what all began?

CHARLES [*moves up to above right end of sofa*]: We were talking too much about Elvira – it's dangerous to have somebody very strongly in your mind when you start dabbling with the occult.

RUTH: She certainly wasn't strongly in my mind.

CHARLES: She was in mine.

RUTH: Oh, she was, was she?

CHARLES [*crosses to face* RUTH *at breakfast table*]: You tried to make me say that she was more physically attractive than you, so that you could hold it over me.

RUTH: I did not. I don't give a hoot how physically attractive she was.

CHARLES: Oh, yes, you do – your whole being is devoured with jealousy.

RUTH [*rises*]: This is too much!

CHARLES [*sits in armchair*]: Women! My God, what I think of women!

RUTH: Your view of women is academic to say the least of it – just because you've always been dominated by them it doesn't necessarily follow that you know anything about them.

CHARLES: I've never been dominated by anyone.

RUTH [*crosses to below Right breakfast chair*]: You were hag-ridden by your mother until you were twenty-three – then you got into the clutches of that awful Mrs Whatever her name was—

CHARLES: Mrs Winthrop-Llewelyn.

RUTH [*clears plates on breakfast table and works round with her back to* CHARLES *to above table*]: I'm not interested. Then there was Elvira – she ruled you with a rod of iron.

CHARLES: Elvira never ruled anyone, she was much too elusive – that was one of her greatest charms . . .

RUTH: Then there was Maud Charteris—

CHARLES: My affair with Maud Charteris lasted exactly seven and a half weeks and she cried all the time.

RUTH: The tyranny of tears – then there was—

CHARLES: If you wish to make an inventory of my sex life, dear, I think it only fair to tell you that you've missed out several episodes – I'll consult my diary and give you the complete list after lunch.

RUTH: It's no use trying to impress me with your routine amorous exploits . . . [*Crosses up stage centre.*]

CHARLES: The only woman in my whole life who's ever attempted to dominate me is you – you've been at it for years.

RUTH: That is completely untrue.

CHARLES: Oh, no, it isn't. You boss me and bully me and order me about – you won't even allow me to have an hallucination if I want to.

RUTH [*comes down stage to* CHARLES *above sofa*]: Charles, alcohol will ruin your whole life if you allow it to get hold of you, you know.

CHARLES [*rises and comes up stage above chair to face* RUTH]: Once and for all, Ruth, I would like you to understand that what happened last night was nothing whatever to do with alcohol. You've very adroitly rationalised the whole affair to your own

191

satisfaction, but your deductions are based on complete fallacy. I am willing to grant you that it was an aberration, some sort of odd psychic delusion brought on by suggestion or hypnosis – I was stone cold sober from first to last and extremely upset into the bargain.

RUTH: *You* were upset indeed? What about me?

CHARLES: You behaved with a stolid, obtuse lack of comprehension that frankly shocked me!

RUTH: I consider that I was remarkably patient. I shall know better next time.

CHARLES: Instead of putting out a gentle comradely hand to guide me – you shouted staccato orders at me like a sergeant-major.

RUTH: You seem to forget that you gratuitously insulted me.

CHARLES: I did not.

RUTH: You called me a guttersnipe – you told me to shut up – and when I quietly suggested that we should go up to bed you said, with the most disgusting leer, that it was an immoral suggestion.

CHARLES [*exasperated*]: I was talking to Elvira!

RUTH: If you were, I can only say that it conjures up a fragrant picture of your first marriage.

CHARLES: My first marriage was perfectly charming and I think it's in the worst possible taste for you to sneer at it.

RUTH: I am not nearly so interested in your first marriage as you think I am. It's your second marriage that is absorbing me at the moment – it seems to me to be on the rocks.

CHARLES: Only because you persist in taking up this ridiculous attitude.

RUTH: My attitude is that of any normal woman whose husband gets drunk and hurls abuse at her.

CHARLES [*crosses to fireplace below sofa, shouting*]: I was not drunk!

RUTH: Be quiet, they'll hear you in the kitchen.

CHARLES: I don't care if they hear me in the Folkestone Town Hall – I was not drunk!

RUTH: Control yourself, Charles.

CHARLES: How can I control myself in the face of your idiotic damned stubbornness? It's giving me claustrophobia.

RUTH: You'd better ring up Dr Bradman.

[EDITH *comes in with a tray to clear away the breakfast things.*]

EDITH: Can I clear, please'm?

RUTH: Yes, Edith. [*Crosses to window*]

EDITH: Cook wants to know about lunch, mum.

RUTH [*coldly*]: Will you be in to lunch, Charles?

CHARLES: Please don't worry about me – I shall be perfectly happy with a bottle of gin in my bedroom.

RUTH: Don't be silly, dear. [*To* EDITH] Tell cook we shall both be in.

EDITH: Yes'm.

RUTH [*conversationally – after a long pause*]: I'm going into Hythe this morning – is there anything you want?

CHARLES: Yes, a great deal – but I doubt if you could get it in Hythe.

RUTH: Tell cook to put Alka-Seltzer down on my list, will you, Edith.

EDITH: Yes'm.

RUTH [*at the window – after another long pause*]: It's clouding over.

CHARLES: You have a genius for understatement.

[*In silence, but breathing heavily,* EDITH *staggers out with the tray.*]

RUTH [*as she goes*]: Don't worry about the table, Edith – I'll put it away.

EDITH: Yes'm

[*When* EDITH *has gone* CHARLES *goes over to* RUTH.]

CHARLES [*coming over to breakfast table to* RUTH *who is folding cloth*]: Please, Ruth – be reasonable.

RUTH: I'm perfectly reasonable.

CHARLES: I wasn't pretending – I really did believe that I saw Elvira and when I heard her voice I was appalled.

RUTH: You put up with it for five years.

[RUTH *puts chairs back up stage Right and down Left.* CHARLES *takes table off stage centre.*]

CHARLES: When I saw her I had the shock of my life – that's why I dropped the glass.

RUTH: But you *couldn't* have seen her.

CHARLES: I know I couldn't have but I *did*.

RUTH [*puts chair up Right*]: I'm willing to concede then that you imagined you did.

CHARLES: That's what I've been trying to explain to you for hours. [*Crosses to mantelpiece*]

RUTH [*to centre below armchair*]: Well then, there's obviously something wrong with you.

CHARLES [*sits on left arm of sofa*]: Exactly – there is something wrong with me – something fundamentally wrong with me – that's why I've been imploring your sympathy and all I got was a sterile temperance lecture.

RUTH: You had been drinking, Charles – there's no denying that.

CHARLES: No more than usual.

RUTH: Well, how do you account for it then?

CHARLES [*frantically*]: I can't account for it – that's what's so awful.

RUTH [*practically*]: Did you feel quite well yesterday – during the day I mean?

CHARLES: Of course I did.

RUTH: What did you have for lunch?

CHARLES: You ought to know, you had it with me.

RUTH [*thinking*]: Let me see now, there was lemon sole and that cheese thing—

CHARLES: Why should having a cheese thing for lunch make me see my deceased wife after dinner?

RUTH: You never know – it was rather rich.

CHARLES: Why didn't you see your dead husband then? You had just as much of it as I did.

RUTH: This is not getting us anywhere at all.

CHARLES: Of course it isn't, and it won't as long as you insist on ascribing supernatural phenomena to colonic irritation.

RUTH: Supernatural grandmother.

CHARLES: I admit she'd have been much less agitating.

RUTH [*standing at back of armchair*]: Perhaps you ought to see a nerve specialist.

CHARLES: I am not in the least neurotic and never have been.

RUTH: A psychoanalyst then.

CHARLES: I refuse to endure months of expensive humiliation only to be told at the end of it that at the age of four I was in love with my rocking-horse.

RUTH: What do you suggest then?

CHARLES: I don't suggest anything – I'm profoundly uneasy.

RUTH [*sits in armchair*]: Perhaps there's something pressing on your brain.

CHARLES: If there were something pressing on my brain I should have violent headaches, shouldn't I?

RUTH: Not necessarily, an uncle of mine had a lump the size of a cricket ball pressing on his brain for years and he never felt a thing.

CHARLES: I know I should know if I had anything like that. [*Rises and goes over to fireplace*]

RUTH: He didn't.

CHARLES: What happened to him?

RUTH: He had it taken out and he's been as bright as a button ever since.

CHARLES: Did he have any sort of delusions – did he think he saw things that weren't there?

RUTH: No, I don't think so.

CHARLES: Well, what the hell are we talking about him for then? It's sheer waste of valuable time.

RUTH: I only brought him up as an example.

CHARLES: I think I'm going mad.

RUTH: How do you feel now?

CHARLES: Physically, do you mean?

RUTH: Altogether.

CHARLES [*after due reflection*]: Apart from being worried I feel quite normal.

RUTH: Good. You're not hearing or seeing anything in the least unusual?

CHARLES: Not a thing.

[ELVIRA *enters by windows carrying a bunch of grey roses. She crosses to writing-table up stage Right and throws zinnias into wastepaper basket and puts her roses into the vase. The roses are as grey as the rest of her.*]

ELVIRA: You've absolutely ruined that border by the sundial – it looks like a mixed salad.

CHARLES: O my God!

RUTH: What's the matter now?

CHARLES: She's here again!

RUTH: What do you mean? – who's here again?

CHARLES: Elvira.

RUTH: Pull yourself together and don't be absurd.

ELVIRA: It's all those nasturtiums – they're so vulgar.

CHARLES: I like nasturtiums.

RUTH: You like what?

ELVIRA [*putting her grey roses into a vase*]: They're all right in moderation but in a mass like that they look beastly.

CHARLES [*crosses over to right of* RUTH *centre*]: Help me, Ruth – you've got to help me—

RUTH [*rises and retreats a pace to left*]: What did you mean about nasturtiums?

CHARLES [*takes* RUTH's *hands and comes round to left of her*]: Never mind about that now – I tell you she's here again.

ELVIRA [*comes to above sofa*]: You have been having a nice scene, haven't you? I could hear you right down the garden.

CHARLES: Please mind your own business.

RUTH: If you behaving like a lunatic isn't my business nothing is.

ELVIRA: I expect it was about me, wasn't it? I know I ought to feel sorry but I'm not – I'm delighted.

CHARLES: How can you be so inconsiderate?

RUTH [*shrilly*]: Inconsiderate! – I like that I must say—

CHARLES: Ruth – darling – please . . .

RUTH: I've done everything I can to help – I've controlled myself admirably – and I should like to say here and now that I don't believe a word about your damned hallucination – you're up to something, Charles – there's been a certain furtiveness in your manner for weeks – why don't you be honest and tell me what it is?

CHARLES: You're wrong – you're dead wrong – I haven't been in the least furtive – I—

RUTH: You're trying to upset me— [*Breaks away from* CHARLES *to Right centre*] For some obscure reason you're trying to goad me into doing something that I might regret – I

won't stand for it any more – you're making me utterly miserable. [*Crosses to sofa and falls into right end of it – she bursts into tears*]

CHARLES [*crosses to* RUTH *Right*]: Ruth – please . . .

RUTH: Don't come near me—

ELVIRA: Let her have a nice cry – it'll do her good. [*Saunters round to down stage Left*]

CHARLES: You're utterly heartless!

RUTH: Heartless!

CHARLES [*wildly*]: I was not talking to you – I was talking to Elvira.

RUTH: Go on talking to her then, talk to her until you're blue in the face but don't talk to me—

CHARLES [*crosses to* ELVIRA *down stage Left*]: Help me, Elvira—

ELVIRA: How?

CHARLES: Make her see you or something.

ELVIRA: I'm afraid I couldn't manage that – it's technically the most difficult business – frightfully complicated, you know – it takes years of study—

CHARLES: You are here, aren't you? You're not an illusion?

ELVIRA: I may be an illusion but I'm most definitely here.

CHARLES: How did you get here?

ELVIRA: I told you last night – I don't exactly know—

CHARLES: Well you must make me a promise that in future you only come and talk to me when I'm alone—

ELVIRA [*pouting*]: How unkind you are – making me feel so unwanted – I've never been treated so rudely . . .

CHARLES: I don't mean to be rude, but you must see—

ELVIRA: It's all your own fault for having married a woman who is incapable of seeing beyond the nose on her face – if she had a grain of real sympathy or affection for you she'd believe what you tell her.

CHARLES: How could you expect anybody to believe this?

ELVIRA: You'd be surprised how gullible people are – we often laugh about it on the other side.

[RUTH, *who has stopped crying and been staring at* CHARLES *in horror, suddenly gets up. As she rises,* CHARLES *crosses to her down stage Right.*]

197

RUTH [*gently*]: Charles—

CHARLES [*surprised at her tone*]: Yes, dear—

RUTH: I'm awfully sorry I was cross—

CHARLES: But, my dear—

RUTH: I understand everything now – I do really—

CHARLES: You do?

RUTH [*patting his arm reassuringly*]: Of course I do.

ELVIRA: Look out – she's up to something—

CHARLES: Will you please be quiet.

RUTH: Of course, darling – we'll all be quiet, won't we? We'll be as quiet as little mice.

CHARLES: Ruth dear, listen—

RUTH: I want you to come upstairs with me and go to bed—

ELVIRA: The way that woman harps on bed is nothing short of erotic.

CHARLES: I'll deal with you later—

RUTH: Very well, darling – come along.

CHARLES: What are you up to?

RUTH: I'm not up to anything – I just want you to go quietly to bed and wait there until Dr Bradman comes—

CHARLES: No, Ruth – you're wrong—

RUTH [*firmly*]: Come, dear—

ELVIRA: She'll have you in a strait-jacket before you know where you are—

CHARLES [*comes to* ELVIRA *– frantically*]: Help me – you must help me—

ELVIRA [*enjoying herself*]: My dear, I would with pleasure, but I can't think how—

CHARLES: I can. [*Back to* RUTH] Listen, Ruth—

RUTH: Yes, dear?

CHARLES: If I promise to go to bed will you let me stay here for five minutes longer?

RUTH: I really think it would be better—

CHARLES: Bear with me – however mad it may seem – bear with me for just five minutes longer—

RUTH [*leaving go of him*]: Very well – what is it?

CHARLES: Sit down.

RUTH [*sitting down*]: All right – there.

CHARLES: Now listen – listen carefully—

ELVIRA: Have a cigarette, it will soothe your nerves.

CHARLES: I don't want a cigarette.

RUTH [*indulgently*]: Then you shan't have one, darling.

CHARLES: Ruth, I want to explain to you clearly and without emotion that beyond any shadow of doubt, the ghost or shade or whatever you like to call it of my first wife Elvira, is in this room now.

RUTH: Yes, dear.

CHARLES: I know you don't believe it and are trying valiantly to humour me but I intend to prove it to you.

RUTH: Why not lie down and have a nice rest and you can prove anything you want to later on.

CHARLES: She may not be here later on.

ELVIRA: Don't worry – she will!

CHARLES: O God!

RUTH: Hush, dear.

CHARLES [*to* ELVIRA]: Promise you'll do what I ask?

ELVIRA: That all depends what it is.

CHARLES [*between them both, facing up stage*]: Ruth – you see that bowl of flowers on the piano?

RUTH: Yes, dear – I did it myself this morning.

ELVIRA: Very untidily if I may say so.

CHARLES: You may not.

RUTH: Very well – I never will again – I promise.

CHARLES: Elvira will now carry that bowl of flowers to the mantelpiece and back again. You will, Elvira, won't you – just to please me?

ELVIRA: I don't really see why I should – you've been quite insufferable to me ever since I materialised.

CHARLES: Please.

ELVIRA: All right, I will just this once – not that I approve of all these Maskelyne and Devant carryings on. [*She goes over to the piano.*]

CHARLES [*crosses to mantelpiece*]: Now, Ruth – watch carefully.

RUTH [*patiently*]: Very well, dear.

CHARLES: Go on, Elvira – take it to the mantelpiece and back again.

[ELVIRA *takes bowl of pansies off piano – brings it slowly down stage below armchair to fire then suddenly pushes it towards* RUTH's *face, who jumps up.*]

RUTH [*furiously*]: How dare you, Charles! You ought to be ashamed of yourself.

CHARLES: What on earth for?

RUTH [*hysterically*]: It's a trick – I know perfectly well it's a trick – you've been working up to this – it's all part of some horrible plan . . .

CHARLES: It isn't – I swear it isn't – Elvira – do something else for God's sake—

ELVIRA: Certainly – anything to oblige.

RUTH [*becoming really frightened*]: You want to get rid of me – you're trying to drive me out of my mind—

CHARLES: Don't be so silly.

RUTH: You're cruel and sadistic and I'll never forgive you . . .

[ELVIRA *waltzes with chair from down stage Left and puts it back and stands above window.*

Ruth makes a dive for the door – crosses between armchair and sofa – CHARLES *follows and catches her up stage Left.*]

I'm not going to put up with this any more—

CHARLES [*holding her*]: You must believe it – you must—

RUTH: Let me go immediately . . .

CHARLES: That was Elvira – I swear it was—

RUTH [*struggling*]: Let me go . . .

CHARLES: Ruth – please—

[RUTH *breaks away to windows.* ELVIRA *shuts them in her face and crosses quickly to mantelpiece.* RUTH *turns.*]

RUTH [*looking at* CHARLES *with eyes of horror*]: Charles – this is madness – sheer madness – it's some sort of auto-suggestion, isn't it – some form of hypnotism, swear to me it's only that – [*Rushes to* CHARLES *centre*] – swear to me it's only that.

ELVIRA [*taking an expensive vase from the mantelpiece and crashing it into the grate*]: Hypnotism my foot!

[RUTH *gives a scream and goes into violent hysterics as—*]

THE CURTAIN FALLS

A few days after the *Blithe Spirit* opening, a deputation of three gentlemen, Filippo del Giudice, Anthony Havelock-Allan and Charles Thorpe, called on me at the Savoy Hotel. I received them warily because I knew that the object of their visit was to persuade me to make a film, and I had no intention of making a film then or at any other time. I had generated in my mind a strong prejudice against the moving-picture business, a prejudice compounded of small personal experience and considerable intellectual snobbery.

The actual proposition they had put to me was that if I agreed to write and appear in a picture for them I should have complete control of cast, director, subject, cameraman, etc., and that all financial aspects would be, they assured me, settled to my satisfaction once I had consented. It would have been churlish not to appreciate that this was a very flattering offer indeed, and although all my instincts were against it, I was forced to admit to myself that, provided I could think of a suitable idea, there was a good deal to be said for it. The very next evening Fate obligingly intervened and rang a bell so loudly in my brain that I was unable to ignore it. I happened to dine in Chester Street with Dickie and Edwina Mountbatten. Dickie had only been home in England for a little over a week, and although I had seen him briefly at the first night of *Blithe Spirit* I had not had an opportunity to talk to him. After dinner, he told me the whole story of the sinking of the *Kelly* off the island of Crete. He told it without apparent emotion, but the emotion was there, poignantly behind every word he uttered. I was profoundly moved and impressed. The Royal Navy means a great deal to me, and here, in this Odyssey of one destroyer, was the very essence of it. All the true sentiment, the comedy, the tragedy, the casual valiance, the unvaunted heroism, the sadness without tears and the pride without end. Later on that night, in my bed at the Savoy, I knew that this was a story to tell if only I could tell it without sentimentality but with simplicity and truth.

In Which We Serve *is the story of a ship, the destroyer H M S Torrin and the men who sail to war in her. We join them when the ship is commissioned in 1939 and follow perhaps a dozen of them through crucial moments in their private lives and service careers.*

Whether showing courage or cowardice, the script is distinguished by its understatement. But there are one or two moments when Coward's pride in the Royal Navy is clearly articulated. At Christmas 1940, for instance, Captain Kinross throws a party to celebrate the engagement of his Signals Officer and persuades his wife, Alix, to propose a toast.

From *IN WHICH WE SERVE*

ALIX: Ladies and gentlemen, I'll begin by taking my husband's advice and wishing you all a very happy Christmas. I'm sure Elizabeth and June will back me up when I say I'm going to deliver, on behalf of all wretched naval wives, a word of warning to Maureen who's been unwise enough to decide to join our ranks.

Dear Maureen, we all wish you every possible happiness but I think it only fair to tell you in advance exactly what you're in for! Speaking from bitter experience, I can only say that the wife of a sailor is most profoundly to be pitied. To begin with, her home life – what there is of it – has no stability whatever. She can never really settle down; she moves through a succession of other people's houses, flats and furnished rooms. She finds herself having to grapple with domestic problems in Bermuda, Malta or Weymouth. We will not deal with the question of pay – that is altogether too painful! What we will deal with is the most important disillusionment of all and that is . . .

KINROSS: Stop her, somebody – this is rank mutiny!

ALIX: . . . and that is – that wherever she goes, there is always in her life a permanent and undefeated rival: her husband's ship. Whether it be a battleship or a sloop, a submarine or a destroyer, it holds first place in his heart. It comes before wife, home, children – everything. Some of us try to fight this and get badly mauled in the process; others, like myself, resign ourselves to the inevitable. That is what you will have to do, my poor Maureen. That is what we all have to do, if we want any peace of mind at all.

Ladies and gentlemen, I give you my rival. It's extraordinary that anyone could be so fond and so proud of their most implacable enemy: this ship. God bless this ship and all who sail in her.

In the following year the Torrin is sunk off Crete and Maureen's husband of only a few months is killed in action. Some of the crew are eventually rescued and taken to Alexandria. Before they part, Captain Kinross addresses the survivors.

KINROSS: I've come to say goodbye to the few of you who are left. We've had so many talks and this is our last. I've always tried to crack a joke or two before and you've all been friendly and laughed at them. But today I'm afraid I've run out of jokes and I don't suppose any of us feels much like laughing.

The *Torrin* has been in one scrap after another but, even when we've had men killed, the majority survived and brought the old ship back. Now she lies in fifteen hundred fathoms and with her more than half our shipmates. If they had to die, what a grand way to go. And now they lie all together with the ship we loved, and they're in very good company. We've lost her but they're still with her.

There may be less than half the *Torrin* left, but I feel that we'll all take up the battle with even stronger heart. Each of us knows twice as much about fighting and each of us has twice as good a reason to fight. You will all be sent to replace men who've been killed in other ships, and the next time you're in action, remember the *Torrin*!

I should like to add that there isn't one of you that I wouldn't be proud and honoured to serve with again. Good-bye, good luck and thank you all from the bottom of my heart.

The film was an enormous popular success and of great propaganda value. It was nominated for two Academy Awards – script and best picture – but, in the event, Coward received a special Oscar for his achievement as writer, producer, co-director, composer and actor. It seemed likely that his name would appear in the New Year's Honours list for 1943 but the accolade he deserved was withheld for more than a quarter of a century.

Throughout his life Coward wrote verse as well as lyrics for his songs. Some of the pieces are no more than pithy comments in rhyme, rather like the telegrams he was fond of sending to his friends, others are substantial narratives. He never described them as poems, insisting that he was not endowed with a true poetic sense. A selection of his verse was published in 1967 but the piece which follows did not appear in book form until 1984. It is, however, a heartfelt reflection on the combatants and non-combatants of the Second World War.

Lie in the Dark and Listen

Lie in the dark and listen,
It's clear tonight so they're flying high
Hundreds of them, thousands perhaps,
Riding the icy, moonlight sky.
Men, material, bombs and maps
Altimeters and guns and charts
Coffee, sandwiches, fleece-lined boots
Bones and muscles and minds and hearts
English saplings with English roots
Deep in the earth they've left below.
Lie in the dark and let them go
Lie in the dark and listen.

Lie in the dark and listen,
They're going over in waves and waves
High above villages, hills and streams
Country churches and little graves
And little citizens' worried dreams.
Very soon they'll have reached the sea
And far below them will lie the bays
And coves and sands where they used to be
Taken for summer holidays.
Lie in the dark and let them go
Lie in the dark and listen.

Lie in the dark and listen,
City magnates and steel contractors,
Factory workers and politicians
Soft, hysterical little actors
Ballet dancers, 'Reserved' musicians,
Safe in your warm, civilian beds.
Count your profits and count your sheep
Life is flying above your heads
Just turn over and try to sleep.
Lie in the dark and let them go
Theirs is a world you'll never know
Lie in the dark and listen.

When he had completed In Which We Serve, *Coward appeared in* Blithe Spirit *for two weeks in order to give his leading man a holiday. It was the first time he had been on a stage for five years. Typically, he next threw himself into a gruelling effort to entertain his fellow-countrymen: a twenty-eight-week tour of the provinces playing the lead in three of his own plays.*

I have tried from the beginning to work constructively for the war effort and now, having been driven back to my own *métier*, the theatre, I cannot work myself up about it any more. This may be sheer escapism, but if I can make people laugh, etc., maybe I am not doing so very badly. I only know that to sit at the side of the stage amid the old familiar sights and sounds and smells is really lovely after all this long time. The only things that matter to me at the moment are whether or not I was good in such and such a scene and if the timing was right and my make-up not too pale. This is my job really, and will remain so through all wars and revolutions and carnage.

(*Diary, 14 September 1942*)

One of the plays, Present Laughter, *provided him with a bravura role as a temperamental matinée idol, Garry Essendine. Garry is enormously attractive to women of all ages and to aspiring theatre students of both sexes.*

PRESENT LAUGHTER

Act I (excerpt)

The scene is GARRY ESSENDINE'S *studio in London. It is about 10.30 in the morning. A young writer called* ROLAND MAULE *has arrived for an interview.*

GARRY: Do sit down, won't you?

ROLAND [*sitting*]: Thank you.

GARRY: Cigarette?

ROLAND: No, thank you.

GARRY: Don't you smoke?

ROLAND: No.

GARRY: Drink?

ROLAND: No, thank you.

GARRY: How old are you?

ROLAND: Twenty-five, why?

GARRY: It doesn't really matter – I just wondered.

ROLAND: How old are you?

GARRY: Forty in December – Jupiter, you know – very energetic.

ROLAND: Yes, of course. [*He gives a nervous, braying laugh.*]

GARRY: You've come all the way from Uckfield?

ROLAND: It isn't very far.

GARRY: Well, it sort of sounds far, doesn't it?

ROLAND [*defensively*]: It's quite near Lewes.

GARRY: Then there's nothing to worry about, is there?

    [MONICA *comes in.*]

GARRY: This is my secretary, Miss Reed – Mr Maule.

MONICA: How do you do – I have your script in the office if you'd like to take it away with you.

ROLAND: Thank you very much.

MONICA: I'll put it in an envelope.

    [MONICA *goes into the office and shuts the door.*

GARRY: I want to talk to you about your play.

ROLAND [*gloomily*]: I expect you hated it.

GARRY: Well, to be candid, I thought it was a little uneven.

ROLAND: I thought you'd say that.

GARRY: I'm glad I'm running so true to form.

ROLAND: I mean, it really isn't the sort of thing you would like, is it?

GARRY: In that case why on earth did you send it to me?

ROLAND: I just took a chance. I mean, I know you only play rather trashy stuff as a rule, and I thought you just might like to have a shot at something deeper.

GARRY: What is there in your play that you consider so deep, Mr Maule? Apart from the plot which is completely submerged after the first four pages.

ROLAND: Plots aren't important, it's ideas that matter. Look at Chekov.

GARRY: In addition to ideas I think we might concede Chekov a certain flimsy sense of psychology, don't you?

ROLAND: You mean my play isn't psychologically accurate?

GARRY [*gently*]: It isn't very good, you know, really, it isn't.

ROLAND: I think it's very good indeed.

GARRY: I understand that perfectly, but you must admit that my opinion, based on a lifelong experience of the theatre, might be the right one.

ROLAND [*contemptuously*]: The commercial theatre.

GARRY: Oh dear. Oh dear. Oh dear!

ROLAND: I suppose you'll say that Shakespeare wrote for the commercial theatre and that the only point of doing anything with the drama at all is to make money! All those old arguments. What you don't realise is that the theatre of the future is the theatre of ideas.

GARRY: That may be, but at the moment I am occupied with the theatre of the present.

ROLAND [*heatedly*]: And what do you do with it? Every play you appear in is exactly the same, superficial, frivolous and without the slightest intellectual significance. You have a great following and a strong personality, and all you do is prostitute yourself every night of your life. All you do with your talent is

207

to wear dressing-gowns and make witty remarks when you might be really helping people, making them think! Making them feel!

GARRY: There can be no two opinions about it. I am having a most discouraging morning.

ROLAND [*rising and standing over* GARRY]: If you want to live in people's memories, to go down to posterity as an important man, you'd better do something about it quickly. There isn't a moment to be lost.

GARRY: I don't give a hoot about posterity. Why should I worry about what people think of me when I'm dead as a doornail, anyway? My worst defect is that I am apt to worry too much about what people think of me when I'm alive. But I'm not going to do that any more. I'm changing my methods and you're my first experiment. As a rule, when insufferable young beginners have the impertinence to criticise me, I dismiss the whole thing lightly because I'm embarrassed for them and consider it not quite fair game to puncture their inflated egos too sharply. But this time, my high-brow young friend, you're going to get it in the neck. To begin with, your play is not a play at all. It's a meaningless jumble of adolescent, pseudo-intellectual poppycock. It bears no relation to the theatre or to life or to anything. And you yourself wouldn't be here at all if I hadn't been bloody fool enough to pick up the telephone when my secretary wasn't looking. Now that you are here, however, I would like to tell you this. If you wish to be a playwright, you just leave the theatre of tomorrow to take care of itself. Go and get yourself a job as a butler in a repertory company if they'll have you. Learn from the ground up how plays are constructed and what is actable and what isn't. Then sit down and write at least twenty plays one after the other, and if you can manage to get the twenty-first produced for a Sunday night performance you'll be damned lucky!

ROLAND [*hypnotised*]: I'd no idea you were like this. You're wonderful!

GARRY [*flinging up his hands*]: My God!

ROLAND: I'm awfully sorry if you think I was impertinent, but

I'm awfully glad too because if I hadn't been you wouldn't
have got angry and if you hadn't got angry I shouldn't have
known what you were really like.

GARRY: You don't in the least know what I'm really like.

ROLAND: Oh, yes, I do – now.

GARRY: I can't see that it matters, anyway.

ROLAND: It matters to me.

GARRY: Why?

ROLAND: Do you really want to know?

GARRY: What on earth are you talking about?

ROLAND: It's rather difficult to explain really.

GARRY: What is difficult to explain?

ROLAND: What I feel about you.

GARRY: But—

ROLAND: No, please let me speak – you see, in a way I've been
rather unhappy about you – for quite a long time – you've
been a sort of obsession with me. I saw you in your last play
forty-seven times, one week I came every night, in the pit,
because I was up in town trying to pass an exam.

GARRY: Did you pass it?

ROLAND: No, I didn't.

GARRY: I'm not entirely surprised.

ROLAND: My father wants me to be a lawyer, that's what the
exam was for, but actually I've been studying psychology a
great deal because I felt somehow that I wasn't at peace with
myself and gradually, bit by bit, I began to realise that you sig-
nified something to me.

GARRY: What sort of something?

ROLAND: I don't quite know – not yet.

GARRY: That 'not yet' is one of the most sinister remarks I've
ever heard.

ROLAND: Don't laugh at me, please. I'm always sick if anyone
laughs at me.

GARRY: You really are the most peculiar young man.

ROLAND: I'm all right now though, I feel fine!

GARRY: I'm delighted.

ROLAND: Can I come and see you again?

GARRY: I'm afraid I'm going to Africa.

ROLAND: Would you see me if I came to Africa too?

GARRY: I really think you'd be happier in Uckfield.

ROLAND: I expect you think I'm mad but I'm not really, I just mind deeply about certain things. But I feel much better now because I think I shall be able to sublimate you all right.

GARRY: Good. Now I'm afraid I shall have to turn you out because I'm expecting my manager and we have some business to discuss.

ROLAND: It's all right. I'm going immediately.

GARRY: Shall I get you your script?

ROLAND: No, no – tear it up – you were quite right about it – it was only written with part of myself, I see that now. Goodbye.

GARRY: Goodbye.

> [ROLAND *goes out.* GARRY *waits until he hears the door slam and then runs to the office door.*]

GARRY: Monica.

MONICA [*entering*]: Has he gone?

GARRY: If ever that young man rings up again, get rid of him at all costs. He's mad as a hatter.

In 1943 Coward brought Present Laughter *and* This Happy Breed *into the West End. These plays had been abandoned in rehearsal in September 1939, and the years between gave the second of them an added resonance. It tells the story of a suburban London family between the armistice at the end of the First World War and the humiliating Munich agreement which preceded the Second.*

Frank and Ethel Gibbons have three children; the younger daughter, Queenie, works in a dress shop and longs to escape from her background, which she sees as common and dull. Billy Mitchell, the boy next door, has loved her since they were children and proposes to her as soon as his career in the Navy allows. She turns him down and runs away with a married man.

Ethel Gibbons disowns her daughter, and Queenie's name is seldom mentioned after that, although Billy remains a friend of the family. Five years later, not long before Christmas, Frank and Ethel have been listening to Edward VIII's abdication speech. Frank Gibbons is about to lock up the house for the night.

THIS HAPPY BREED

Act III

SCENE 1

SCENE: *The dining-room of the Gibbons' house, Number 17 Sycamore Road, Clapham Common.*
TIME: 10 December 1936.

There is a tap on the window.

ETHEL: That'll be Bob. Now I can get on with me darning.
  [FRANK *goes to the window, opens it and admits* BILLY. BILLY *is now thirty-four and wearing the uniform of a Warrant Officer. He has grown a little more solid with the years, but apart from this there is not much change in him.*]
FRANK: Well, here's a surprise!
BILLY: Hallo, Mr Gibbons.
ETHEL: Why, Billy – I'd no idea you was back.
BILLY [*shaking hands with her*]: I've been transferred from a cruiser to a destroyer – I've got a couple of weeks' leave.
FRANK: D'you like that?
BILLY: You bet I do.
FRANK: What's the difference?
BILLY: Oh, lots of little things. To start with I live in the ward-room – then I keep watches when we're at sea – and well, it's sort of more friendly, if you know what I mean.
FRANK: Like a drink?
BILLY: No, thanks. I just had one with Dad.
ETHEL: Is he coming in?
BILLY: Yes, I think so – a bit later on.
ETHEL: He must be glad you're back. It must be lonely for him in that house all by himself since your mother was taken.
FRANK: Nora DIED, Ethel! Nobody took her.

ETHEL: You ought to be ashamed, talking like that in front of Billy.

BILLY: It was a blessed release really, you know, Mrs Gibbons, what with one thing and another. She'd been bedridden so long—

FRANK: Hear the speech?

BILLY: Yes.

FRANK: What did you think of it?

BILLY: Oh, I don't know – a bit depressing – taken all round. He was popular in the Service, you know.

FRANK: Yes – I expect he was.

BILLY: He came on board a ship I was in once, in the Mediterranean, that was about five years ago when I was still a T.G.M.

ETHEL: What's that?

BILLY: Torpedo Gunner's Mate.

FRANK: All them initials in the Navy. I can't think how you remember 'em.

BILLY: Oh, you get used to it.

ETHEL: Would you like me to go and make you a cup of tea? It won't take a minute.

BILLY: No, thanks, Mrs Gibbons – there's something I want to talk to you about as a matter of fact – both of you.

FRANK: All right, Son – what is it?

BILLY [*nervously*]: Got a cigarette on you? I left mine next door.

FRANK [*producing a packet*]: Here you are.

BILLY [*taking one*]: Thanks.

FRANK: Match?

BILLY [*striking one of his own*]: Got one, thanks.

FRANK [*after a slight pause*]: Well?

BILLY: I feel a bit awkward really – I wanted Dad to come with me and back me up, but he wouldn't.

FRANK: A man of your age hanging on to his father's coat-tails, I never 'eard of such a thing. What have you been up to?

ETHEL [*with sudden premonition, sharply*]: What is it, Billy?

BILLY: It's about Queenie.

[*There is silence for a moment.*]

ETHEL [*hardening*]: What about her?

BILLY: Does it still make you angry – even to hear her name?

ETHEL: I'm not angry.

FRANK: Have you seen her, Billy?

BILLY: Yes – I've seen her.

FRANK [*eagerly*]: How is she?

BILLY: Fine.

[*There is another silence.* BILLY *mooches about the room a bit.*]

ETHEL [*with an obvious effort*]: What is it that you wanted to say about Queenie, Billy?

BILLY [*in a rush*]: I sympathise with how you feel, Mrs Gibbons – really I do – and what's more she does too. She knows what a wrong she did you in going off like that. It didn't take her long to realise it. She hasn't had any too good a time, you know. In fact, she's been through a good deal. He left her – the man she went off with – Major Blount – after about a year. He went back to his wife. He left Queenie stranded in a sort of boarding-house in Brussels.

ETHEL [*bitterly*]: How soon was it before she found another man to take her on?

FRANK: Ethel!

BILLY: A long time – over three years.

ETHEL: [*bending over her darning*]: She's all right now then, isn't she?

BILLY: Yes – she's all right now.

FRANK: What sort of a bad time did she have – how d'you mean?

BILLY: Trying to earn a living for herself – getting in and out of different jobs. She showed dresses off in a dressmaker's shop for over a year, I believe, but the shop went broke, and then she got herself a place to look after some English children. It wasn't a very long job. She just had to take them across France to Marseilles and put on a ship to go out to their parents in India. By that time she had a little money saved and was coming home to England to try and get her old manicuring job back when she got ill with appendicitis and was taken to hospital—

FRANK: Where – where was she taken to hospital? How long ago?

BILLY: Paris – about a year ago. Then, when she was in the hospital she picked up with an old Scotswoman who was in the next bed and a little while later the two of them started an old English tea room in Menton in the South of France – you know, just for the English visitors – that's where I ran into her by accident. We were doing a summer cruise and the ship I was in laid off a place called Villefranche for a few days. A couple of pals and I hired a taxi to go for a drive and stopped at Menton to have a cup of tea – and there she was!

ETHEL: Is she there now?

BILLY: No, she isn't there now.

FRANK: Where is she then?

BILLY: She's here.

ETHEL: Here!

FRANK: How d'you mean – here?

BILLY: Next door with Dad.

ETHEL [*jumping to her feet and dropping her darning on the floor*]: Billy!

BILLY: We were married last week in a registry office in Plymouth.

ETHEL: Married!

BILLY [*simply*]: I've always loved her, you know – I always said I'd wait for her.

FRANK [*brokenly*]: O Son – I can't believe it – O Son! [*He wrings BILLY's hand wildly and then almost runs out through the french windows.*]

BILLY: You'll forgive her now, won't you, Mrs Gibbons?

ETHEL [*in a strained voice*]: I don't seem to have any choice, do I?

BILLY: I always thought you'd like to have me for a son—

ETHEL: Better late than never – that's what it is, isn't it? [*She starts half laughing and crying at the same time.*] Better late than – never – oh dear!—

[*He takes her in his arms and after holding her close for a moment, places her gently in the chair.*]

BILLY: Shall I get you a little nip of something?

ETHEL [*tearfully*]: Yes, please—

BILLY: Where is it?

ETHEL: In the sideboard cupboard.

[*BILLY goes quickly to the sideboard, opens the cupboard, takes a bottle of whisky out and pours some, neat, into a glass. He*

brings it to her. He gives her the glass and she sips a little. He
takes her left hand and pats it affectionately.
  FRANK *comes back through the window leading* QUEENIE
by the hand. She is soberly dressed and looks pale. There is a
strained silence for a moment.]
QUEENIE: Hallo, Mum.
ETHEL: So you've come back, have you – you bad girl.
QUEENIE [*coming slowly across the room to her*]: Yes, Mum.
ETHEL [*putting her arms round her*]: A nice way to behave, I must
  say – upsetting me like this—

THE LIGHTS FADE

In the later stages of the war Coward followed Churchill's advice
and went to entertain the troops. He bounced around the Middle East,
Australia and New Zealand, South Africa, Burma, India and Ceylon,
wherever he could do some good. Inevitably, this stretched his stamina
to the limit and, in order to avoid a breakdown, he needed some occa-
sional respite. So it was that in 1944 he paid his first visit to an island
that was eventually to become his home.

In the old days the house had been the property of the resident
Admiral, and at one time Nelson, shivering and racked with
fever, was conveyed to it on a litter to regain his health in the
cooler air and fresher breezes. Although I was not, like Nelson,
shivering and racked with fever, I was certainly overtired and
stuffed with catarrh and I hoped that the cooler air and fresher
breezes would do as good a job on me as they had on him. I was
received by a smiling, dusky majordomo called Montgomery,
and several other equally smiling and equally dusky characters,
and when I had explored the house and garden, I settled myself
in a hammock slung between an orange tree and a coco-palm
and felt peace already beginning.

Later in the day a brisk young woman called Florence Reed
appeared with a piano. She was private secretary to Robert Kirkwood, to whom I had a letter of introduction, and it was she who
had corralled the staff and put the house in order to receive me.

She also had been sworn to secrecy and assured me that although it was already known by the grapevine intelligence that a mysterious gentleman had arrived at Bellevue, no one had the slightest idea who it was. From then on, apart from Florence, two American soldier friends of hers and Sybil and Bobby Kirkwood, I met no one in Jamaica until a day or two before I left. It was a perfect holiday. The house was comfortable, the garden lovely and there were masses of books to read. I sat each evening on the terrace watching the sun set and the lights come up in the town. On the third night the moon was full and fireflies flickered among the silvered trees, in fact no magic was omitted. The spell was cast and held, and I knew I should come back.

By the end of the first week my catarrh had gone, my voice had come back and I was satisfactorily sun-tanned and feeling better than I had felt for ages. The creative urge, seldom long in abeyance, reared its sprightly head again and I wrote a song called 'Uncle Harry'. It was a gay song and I hammered it out interminably on Florence's piano until it was so firmly stamped on my memory that I knew I couldn't forget it. I don't suppose that Montgomery and the staff have forgotten it either.

'Uncle Harry' had to wait until the war was over to be heard on the stage. It was destined to be the sole survivor of one of Coward's rare failures, the operetta Pacific 1860. *Meanwhile he discovered another aspect of celebrity.*

The nine o'clock news announced the discovery of the German blacklist. Among the people to be dealt with when England was invaded were Winston, Vic Oliver, Sybil Thorndike, Rebecca West and me. What a cast!

(Diary, 13 September 1945)

Pacific 1860 *opened in December 1946 with Mary Martin making her London début and a cast which included Sylvia Cecil and Graham Payn. Two consecutive diary entries tell a sad story.*

Thursday A hectic, strained day. Worked on lighting until 4.30. Came home, had a bath and changed into tails and went to the

216

theatre. A really triumphant first night. Mary wonderful; Sylvia Cecil stopped the show; Graham magnificent.

Friday   The blackest and beastliest day of the year. To begin with, a blast of abuse in the Press. Not one good notice, the majority being frankly vile. I don't usually mind but I am over-tired.

(Diary, 19–20 December 1946)

Only 'Uncle Harry' lived on to become a regular part of Coward's cabaret repertoire.

Uncle Harry

Verse 1

We all of us have relations,
Our crosses in life we bear,
A gloomy group of uncles, cousins and aunts,
We meet them in railway stations,
In Harrods or Chester Square,
And always on the Channel boat to France.
We have to be polite to them,
They sometimes send us pheasants,
We always have to write to them
To thank for Christmas presents.
These family obligations
Admittedly are a bore
But I possess one uncle that I positively adore.

Refrain 1

Poor Uncle Harry
Wanted to be a missionary
So he took a ship and sailed away.
This visionary,
Hotly pursued by dear Aunt Mary,
Found a South Sea Isle on which to stay.
The natives greeted them kindly and invited them to dine

On yams and clams and human hams and vintage coconut wine,
The taste of which was filthy but the after-effects divine.
Poor Uncle Harry
Got a bit gay and longed to tarry.
This, Aunt Mary couldn't quite allow,
She lectured him severely on a number of church affairs
But when she'd gone to bed he made a getaway down the stairs,
For he longed to find the answer to a few of the maiden's prayers.
Uncle Harry's not a missionary now.

Poor Uncle Harry
After a chat with dear Aunt Mary
Thought the time had come to make a row,
He lined up all the older girls in one of the local sheds
And while he was reviling them and tearing himself to shreds
They took their Mother Hubbards off and tied them round their
    heads.
Uncle Harry's not a missionary now.
He's awfully happy
But he's certainly not a missionary now!

Verse 2

Now Uncle was just a 'seeker',
A 'dreamer' sincerely blest,
Of this there couldn't be a shadow of doubt.
The fact that his flesh was weaker
Than even Aunt Mary guessed
Took even her some time to figure out.
In all those languid latitudes
The atmosphere's exotic,
To take up moral attitudes
Would be too idiotic,
Though nobody could be meeker
Than Uncle had been before
I bet today he's giving way
At practically every pore!

Refrain 2

Poor Uncle Harry
Having become a missionary
Found the natives' morals rather crude.
He and Aunt Mary
Quickly imposed an arbitrary
Ban upon them shopping in the nude.
They all considered this silly and they didn't take it well,
They burnt his boots and several suits and wrecked the Mission
    Hotel,
They also burnt his mackintosh, which made a disgusting smell.
Poor Uncle Harry
After some words with dear Aunt Mary
Called upon the chiefs for a pow-wow.
They didn't brandish knives at him, they really were awfully sweet,
They made concerted dives at him and offered him things to eat,
But when they threw their wives at him he had to admit defeat.
Uncle Harry's not a missionary now.

Poor dear Aunt Mary
Though it were revolutionary
Thought *her* time had come to take a bow.
Poor Uncle Harry looked at her, in whom he had placed his trust,
His very last illusion broke and crumbled away to dust
For she'd placed a flower behind her ear and frankly exposed her
    bust.
Uncle Harry's not a missionary now.
He's left the island
But he's certainly not a missionary now.

Sadly, Pacific 1860 *set a pattern for the fate of Coward's post-war musicals. He started each one in the high hope of producing a success to equal that of* Bitter Sweet. *In the event none of them came within striking distance, although there are songs to remember in each of them. His later triumphs arrived from other directions, and his spirits were restored by the acquisition of a new home. In 1948 he returned to Jamaica and, almost as soon as he arrived, recorded in his diary his*

219

feeling of peace and contentment. 'Something tells me', he wrote, 'that the time has come to make a few plans for escape in the future.' A month later the plans were made.

Monday   The die is cast. Now I must really admit how excited I am. If we dynamite the cove, it will bring white sand in. Sure it is a good buy. We stayed behind on the point and watched the sunset gilding the mountains and the sea. We also saw a double rainbow and for a few moments the whole land was bathed in a pinky gold light. We drove home through the spectacular sunset and I thought of a name for the house, Blue Harbour. It is a good name because it sounds nice and really describes the view. The house is to be built against the hill on different levels. It will be ready in December. I am very happy.

Tuesday   Mother's and Hitler's birthday. Worked a bit and lay in the sun.

Sunday   Graham's birthday, which we celebrated by going down to the lawyer and signing formally the contract for the land. I am now a property owner in Jamaica and it is jolly fine.

(Diary, 19, 20 and 25 April 1948)

Jamaica

Jamaica's an island surrounded by sea
(Like Corsica, Guam and Tasmania)
The tourist does not need to wear a topee
Or other macabre miscellanea.
Remember that this is a tropical place
Where violent hues are abundant
And bright coloured clothes with a bright yellow face
Look, frankly, a trifle redundant.
A simple ensemble of trousers and shirt
Becomes both the saint and the sinner
And if a head waiter looks bitterly hurt
You *can* wear a jacket for dinner.

Jamaica's an island surrounded by sea
(It shares this distinction with Elba)
Its easy to order a goat fricassee
But madness to ask for Pêche Melba.
You'll find (to the best of this writer's belief)
That if you want rice you can get it
But visitors ordering mutton or beef
Will certainly live to regret it.
There's seldom a shortage of ackees and yams
Or lobsters, if anyone's caught them
But if you've a passion for imported hams
You'd bloody well better import them.

Jamaica's an island surrounded by sea
(It has this in common with Cuba)
Its national tunes, to a certain degree,
Are founded on Boop-boop-a-duba.
'Neath tropical palms under tropical skies
Where equally tropical stars are
The vocal Jamaicans betray no surprise
However off-key their guitars are.
The native Calypsos which seem to be based
On hot-air-conditioned reflexes
Conclusively prove that to people of taste
There's nothing so funny as sex is.

Jamaica's an island surrounded by sea
(Like Alderney, Guernsey and Sark are)
Its wise not to dive with exuberant glee
Where large barracuda and shark are.
The reefs are entrancing, the water is clear,
The colouring couldn't be dreamier
But one coral scratch and you may spend a year
In bed with acute septicaemia.
The leading hotels are extremely well run
The service both cheerful and dextrous
But even the blisters you get from the sun
Are firmly included as extras.

Jamaica's an island surrounded by sea
(*Unlike* Ecuador or Guiana)
The tourist may not have a 'Fromage de Brie'
But always can have a banana.
He also can have, if he has enough cash,
A pleasantly rum-sodden liver
And cure his rheumatic complaints in a flash
By shooting himself at Milk River.
In fact every tourist who visits these shores
Can thank his benevolent Maker
For taking time off from the rest of His chores
To fashion the Isle of Jamaica.

At the end of the Forties, Coward was as busy as ever in the theatre and films. He wrote three new plays and a screenplay in which he appeared himself, as well as reviving Present Laughter *in London and playing it in French in Brussels and Paris. Over Christmas 1949 he was in Jamaica working on a new musical.*

Woke bright and early with a wonderful idea for the show. I am going to do the whole thing virtually in one set – the night-club. There can be a couple of insets and a scrim if I need them, but the story must be the club and what happens in it. Pinkie is the star of it and is being kept by the man who runs it. Harry is the sailor she falls in love with, has an affair with and finally renounces. This set-up will give perfect opportunities for all the numbers because those not in the story can be done in the floor show. One principal built set will minimise the cost of production. In fact it really is a very good idea indeed. The title is *Ace of Clubs*.

(*Diary, 27 December 1949*)

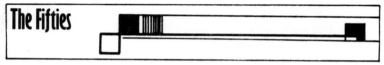

Although Coward continued to write both plays and musicals, the
Fifties brought him his greatest success in cabaret. His new musical,
Ace of Clubs, opened in July 1950 and contained one number which
was to prove particularly prophetic for the new decade.

I Like America

Verse 1

HARRY: I don't care for China,
      Japan's far too small,
      I've rumbled the Rio Grande,
      I hate Asia Minor,
      I can't bear Bengal
      And I shudder to think
      Of the awful stink
      On the road to Samarkand.

GIRLS: The heat and smell
      Must be sheer hell
      On the road to Samarkand.

HARRY: I like America,
      I have played around
      Every slappy-happy hunting ground
      But I find America – okay.
      I've been about a bit
      But I must admit
      That I didn't know the half of it
      Till I hit the U S A.
      No likely lass
      In Boston, Mass.
      From passion will recoil.
      In Dallas, Tex.

They talk of sex
But only think of oil.
New Jersey dames
Go up in flames
If someone mentions – bed.
In Chicago, Illinois
Any girl who meets a boy
Giggles and shoots him dead!
But I like America
Its Society
Offers infinite variety
And come what may
I shall return some day
To the good old U S A.

Verse 2

I've loathed every acre
From Cannes to Canton,
I also deplore Bombay,
I've jeered at Jamaica
And seen through Ceylon,
And exploded the myth
Of those Flying Fith
On the Road to Mandalay.

GIRLS: We'll never mith
Those blasted fith
On the Road to Mandalay.

HARRY: But I like America,
I have travelled far
From Northumberland to Zanzibar
And I find America – okay.
I've roamed the Spanish Main
Eaten sugar-cane
But I never tasted cellophane
Till I struck the U S A.
All delegates

From Southern States
Are nervy and distraught.
In New Orleans
The wrought-iron screens
Are dreadfully overwrought.
Beneath each tree
In Tennessee
Erotic books are read.
And when alligators thud
Through the Mississippi mud
Sex rears its ugly head.
But – I like America,
Every scrap of it,
All the sentimental crap of it
And come what may
Give me a holiday
In the good old U S A.

Ace of Clubs *ran for most of 1950 but was hardly a huge success. The best theatrical offer Coward received that year was to direct and star in* The King and I *opposite Gertrude Lawrence on Broadway. Much to the financial satisfaction of John van Druten and Yul Brynner, who eventually divided the chores between them, he turned down both opportunities in that great money-spinner.*

The Fifties were the years of the intimate revue, a form which suited Coward even better than the elaborate song-and-dance spectacles which he wrote in the Twenties and Thirties. He contributed to both The Lyric Revue *(1951) and* The Globe Revue *(1952) songs which were very useful to him in his subsequent cabaret performances. The two numbers which follow provide a potted social history of England in that rather bleak period, although after more than forty years the first of them may need a little explanation.*

In 1951 the British people were encouraged to celebrate the centenary of the Great Exhibition of Victorian times and announce to the world our twentieth-century supremacy in science and the arts. Coward was asked to serve on one of the many planning committees but eventually resigned in protest at its 'shambolic bureaucracy'. So when the Festival opened on the south bank of the Thames, he went as a visitor and judged it to be 'the last word in squalor and completely un-gay'. But Gerald Barry, the director-general of the whole frantic fun fair, did get his knighthood and we have a handsome concert hall to remind us of the Festival.

Don't Make Fun of the Fair

Verse 1

We're proud to say
In every way
We're ordinary folk,
But please to observe
We still preserve
Our sturdy hearts of oak.
Although as servants of the state
We may have been coerced,
As we've been told to celebrate
We'll celebrate or burst.
Though while we brag
Our shoulders sag
Beneath a heavy yoke
We all get terribly heated
If it's treated
As a joke. So:

Refrain 1

Don't make fun of the festival,
Don't make fun of the fair,
We down-trodden British must learn to be skittish
And give an impression of devil-may-care
To the wide wide world,
We'll sing 'God for Harry',
And if it turns out all right
Knight Gerald Barry.
Clear the national decks, my lads,
Everyone of us counts,
Grab the travellers' cheques, my lads,

And pray that none of them bounce.
Boys and Girls come out to play,
Every day in every way
Help the tourist to defray
All that's underwritten.
Sell your rations and overcharge,
And don't let anyone sabotage
Our own dear Festival of Britain.

Verse 2

We've never been
Exactly keen
On showing off or swank
But as they say
That gay display
Means money in the bank,
We'll make the dreadful welkin ring
From Penge to John O'Groats
And cheer and laugh and shout and sing
Before we cut our throats,
We know we're caught
And must support
This patriotic prank
And though we'd rather have shot ourselves
We've got ourselves
To thank. So:

Refrain 2

Don't make fun of the festival,
Don't make fun of the fair,
We must pull together in spite of the weather
That dampens our spirits and straightens our hair.
Let the people sing
Even though they shiver
Roses red and noses mauve
Over the river.
Though the area's fairly small,
Climb Discovery's Dome,

Take a snooze in the concert hall,
At least it's warmer than home.
March about in funny hats,
Show the foreign diplomats
That our proletariat's
Milder than a kitten.
We believe in the right to strike,
But now we've bloody well got to like
Our own dear Festival of Britain.

Refrain 3

Don't make fun of the festival,
Don't make fun of the fair,
We must have a look at a cookery book
To prevent us from spreading alarm and despair.
We can serve whale steaks
When the weather's hotter
And in place of entrecôtes,
What's wrong with otter?
Greet the gala with fervence, boys,
Learn to dance in the dark,
Build the Sunday Observance boys
A shrine in Battersea Park.
Cross your fingers, hold your thumbs,
Blow your trumpets, roll your drums,
Even if nobody comes
Don't be conscience-smitten.
If no overseas trade appears
We'll have to work for a thousand years
To pay for the Festival of Britain.

Refrain 4

Don't make fun of the festival,
Don't make fun of the fair.
We mustn't look glum when the visitors come
And discover our cupboard is ever so bare.
We must cheer, boys, cheer,
Look as though we love it

And if it should be a bust
Just rise above it.
Take a nip from your brandy flask,
Scream and caper and shout,
Don't give anyone time to ask
What the Hell it's about.
Face the future undismayed,
Pray for further Marshall Aid,
Have the toast from *Cavalcade*
Drastically rewritten.
Peace and dignity we may lack,
But wave a jolly Trades Union Jack,
Hurrah for the festival,
We'll pray for the festival,
Hurrah for the Festival of Britain!

Refrain 5

Don't make fun of the festival,
Don't make fun of the fair,
Our Government bosses
Are counting their losses
And one of them's taken to brushing his hair.
We must all salute – those who double-crossed us,
Fire a round
For every pound
Ground-nuts have cost us,
Blow a kiss to the Board of Trade,
Learn to laugh like a drain
If a million has been mislaid,
Who are we to complain?
Join our civil servants' ball,
Cheer our near Decline and Fall,
Gibbon might have dreamed it all,
Also Bulwer-Lytton.
If our workers begin to slack
Let's get some enemy aliens back,
Hurrah for the Festival of Britain!

There Are Bad Times Just Around the Corner

Verse 1

They're out of sorts in Sunderland
And terribly cross in Kent,
They're dull in Hull
And the Isle of Mull
Is seething with discontent,
They're nervous in Northumberland
And Devon is down the drain,
They're filled with wrath
On the Firth of Forth
And sullen on Salisbury Plain,
In Dublin they're depressed, lads,
Maybe because they're Celts
For Drake is going West, lads,
And so is everyone else.
Hurray – hurray – hurray!
Misery's here to stay.

Refrain 1

There are bad times just around the corner,
There are dark clouds hurtling through the sky
And it's no good whining
About a silver lining
For we know from experience that they won't roll by.
With a scowl and a frown
We'll keep our peckers down
And prepare for depression and doom and dread,
We're going to unpack our troubles from our old kit bag
And wait until we drop down dead.

Verse 2

From Portland Bill to Scarborough
They're querulous and subdued
And Shropshire lads
Have behaved like cads

From Berwick-on-Tweed to Bude,
They're mad at Market Harborough
And livid at Leigh-on-Sea,
In Tunbridge Wells
You can hear the yells
Of woe-begone bourgeoisie.
We all get bitched about, lads,
Whoever our vote elects,
We know we're up the spout, lads,
And that's what England expects.
Hurray – hurray – hurray!
Trouble is on the way.

Refrain 2

There are bad times just around the corner,
The horizon's gloomy as can be,
There are black birds over
The grayish cliffs of Dover
And the rats are preparing to leave the B B C.
We're an *un*happy breed
And very bored indeed
When reminded of something that Nelson said.
While the press and the politicians nag nag nag
We'll wait until we drop down dead.

Verse 3

From Colwyn Bay to Kettering
They're sobbing themselves to sleep,
The shrieks and wails
In the Yorkshire dales
Have even depressed the sheep.
In rather vulgar lettering
A very disgruntled group
Have posted bills
On the Cotswold Hills
To prove that we're in the soup.
While begging Kipling's pardon
There's one thing we know for sure

If England is a garden
We ought to have more manure.
Hurray – hurray – hurray!
Suffering and dismay.

Refrain 3

There are bad times just around the corner
And the outlook's absolutely vile,
There are Home Fires smoking
From Windermere to Woking
And we're *not* going to tighten our belts and smile smile smile,
At the sound of a shot
We'd just as soon as not
Take a hot water bottle and go to bed,
We're going to *un*tense our muscles till they sag sag sag
And wait until we drop down dead.

Refrain 4

There are bad times just around the corner,
We can all look forward to despair,
It's as clear as crystal
From Bridlington to Bristol
That we can't save democracy and we don't much care,
If the Reds and the Pinks
Believe that England stinks
And that world revolution is bound to spread,
We'd better all learn the lyrics of the old 'Red Flag'
And wait until we drop down dead.
A likely story
Land of Hope and Glory,
Wait until we drop down dead.

In 1952 Coward was asked if he would like to adapt Pygmalion *as a musical for Mary Martin. He turned it down and four years later, as the whole world knows, Lerner and Loewe picked up the notion, although not for Miss Martin. In 1953 Coward had the excellent idea of basing a musical on* Lady Windermere's Fan. *This was staged a year later under the title* After the Ball *but, due to a series of misfortunes in pro-*

duction, never met with the success it deserved. Of the many songs which ought to survive, 'Mr Hopper's Chanty' is one, a fascinating example of the writer spinning his own brilliant invention for a character who has little to do in Wilde's original but springs to life as a song-and-dance man.

Mr Hopper's Chanty

MR HOPPER: My Grandpa landed from a convict ship
On the beach of Botany Bay.

OTHERS: Haul away; haul away; how peculiar people are,
Fancy landing Grandpapa
On the beach of Botany Bay.

MR HOPPER: He didn't strike oil and he didn't strike gold
But he lived to be very very very very old
In a rather disgusting way.

MR GRAHAM: What a curious thing to say!

MR HOPPER: My Grandma's meeting with this gay young rip
Was achieved on the very first day.

OTHERS: Haul away; haul away; having travelled all that far
Fancy meeting Grandmama
On the beach on the very first day!

MR HOPPER: She happened to be, when he landed there,
Combing her fuzzy-wuzzy blue-black hair
And he sprang at her straight away.

MR DUMBY: Steady, old man, Fair Play!

MR HOPPER: They lay on the sand of that alien land
Where the wallabies gaily frisk
And plighted their troth, in a way that was both
Effective and fairly brisk.

MR GRAHAM: He ran an appalling risk!

MR HOPPER: And the net result of the whole affair
You can perfectly plainly see
By my coloured skin and kinky hair
That I'm half aboriginee.

MR DUMBY: What a socially regrettable, un-Debrettable,
Maddening thing to be!

MR HOPPER: It's a solemn thought for a son and heir
To know who his forebears really were
And whether or not you know or care
Before my Dad was a millionaire
We lived . . .

OTHERS: Where?

MR HOPPER: In our family tree!

OTHERS: Haul away; haul away;
My goodness gracious me!

MR HOPPER: I can see my brothers and sisters now
Swinging about from bough to bough
On the very, very top . . .

OTHERS: For heaven's sake stop!

MR HOPPER: The top of our family tree!

Coward began a new career as a cabaret performer at the Café de Paris in 1951 and his first-night audience included Princess Margaret and the Duchess of Kent. The diary reads, 'Really triumphant success – tore the place up!'. Three years later he was ushering another international star down that famous staircase.

Marlene arrived on Wednesday and there was a tremendous

to-do. She looked ravishing and was mobbed and fussed over and photographed. I took her to *After the Ball* which she didn't care for much. She opens tomorrow night, and I am writing a little verse with which to introduce her.

(Diary, 20 June 1954)

Tribute to Marlene Dietrich

We know God made trees
And the birds and the bees
And the seas for the fishes to swim in,
We are also aware
That he has quite a flair
For creating exceptional women.
When Eve said to Adam
'Start calling me Madam'
The world became far more exciting,
Which turns to confusion
The modern delusion
That sex is a question of lighting.
For female allure
Whether pure or impure
Has seldom reported a failure
As I know and you know
From Venus and Juno
Right down to La Dame aux Camélias.
This glamour, it seems,
Is the substance of dreams
To the most imperceptive perceiver,
The Serpent of Nile
Could achieve with a smile
Far quicker results than Geneva.
Though we all might enjoy
Seeing Helen of Troy
As a gay, cabaret entertainer,
I doubt that she could
Be one quarter as good
As our legendary, lovely Marlene.

*Later that year Coward was back at the Café de Paris himself,
singing one of the best of his later comedy numbers.*

I opened triumphantly at the Café de Paris last Monday. I wasn't
particularly nervous; there was nothing wrong with my voice
and I really did tear the place up. The new songs all went won-
derfully and 'Piccola Marina' is obviously a rouser. Everybody
was there and it was a highly satisfactory evening.

(Diary, 24 October 1954)

A Bar on the Piccola Marina

Verse

In a 'bijou' abode
In St Barnabas Road
Not far from the Esher by-pass
Lived a mother and wife
Who, most of her life,
Let every adventure fly past.
She had two strapping daughters and a rather dull son
And a much duller husband who at sixty-one
Elected to retire
And, later on, expire,
Sing Hallelujah, Hey nonny-no, Hey nonny-no, Hey nonny-no!
He joined the feathered choir.
On a wet afternoon
In the middle of June
They all of them came home soaking
Having laid him to rest
By special request
In the family vault at Woking,
And then in the middle of the funeral wake
With her mouth full of excellent Madeira cake
His widow cried, 'That's done,
My life's at last begun,
Sing Hallelujah, Hey nonny-no, Hey nonny-no, Hey nonny-no,
It's time I had some fun,

236

Today, though hardly a jolly day,
At least has set me free,
We'll all have a lovely holiday
On the island of Capri!'

Refrain 1

In a bar on the Piccola Marina
Life called to Mrs Wentworth-Brewster,
Fate beckoned her and introduced her
Into a rather queer
Unfamiliar atmosphere.
She'd just sit there, propping up the bar
Beside a fisherman who sang to a guitar.
When accused of having gone too far
She merely cried, 'Funiculi!
Just fancy me!
Funicula!'
When he bellowed *'Che Bella Signorina!'*
Sheer ecstasy at once produced a
Wild shriek from Mrs Wentworth-Brewster,
Changing her whole demeanour.
When both her daughters and her son said,
'Please come home, Mama,'
She murmured rather bibulously, 'Who d'you think you are?'
Nobody can afford to be so lahdy-bloody-da
In a bar on the Piccola Marina.

Interlude

Every fisherman cried.
'Viva viva' and *'Che ragazza'*,
When she sat in the Grand Piazza
Everybody would rise,
Every fisherman sighed,
'Viva viva che bell' Inglesi',
Someone even said, 'Whoops-adaisy!'
Which was quite a surprise.
Each night she'd make some gay excuse
And beaming with good will

She'd just slip into something loose
And totter down the hill.

Refrain 2

To the bar on the Piccola Marina
Where love came to Mrs Wentworth-Brewster,
Hot flushes of delight suffused her,
Right round the bend she went,
Picture her astonishment,
Day in, day out she would gad about
Because she felt she was no longer on the shelf,
Night out, night in, knocking back the gin
She'd cry, 'Hurrah!
Funicula
Funiculi
Funic yourself!'
Just for fun three young sailors from Messina
Bowed low to Mrs Wentworth-Brewster,
Said *'Scusi'* and politely goosed her.
Then there was quite a scena.
Her family, in floods of tears, cried,
'Leave these men, Mama.'
She said, 'They're just high-spirited, like all Italians are,
And most of them have a great deal more to offer than Papa
In a bar on the Piccola Marina.'

'Tearing the place up' became quite a habit with Coward in the Fifties. Never more so than in Nevada on a legendary night in June 1955 . . .

Well, it is all over bar the shouting which is still going on. I have made one of the most sensational successes of my career and to pretend that I am not absolutely delighted would be idiotic. I have had screaming rave notices and the news has flashed round the world. I am told continually, verbally and in print, that I am the greatest attraction that Las Vegas has ever had and that I am the greatest performer in the world, etc., etc. It is all very, very exciting and generous, and when I look back at the grudging

238

dreariness of the English newspaper gentlemen announcing, when I first opened at the Café de Paris, that I massacred my own songs, I really feel that I don't want to appear at home much more.

The first night, from the social–theatrical point of view, was fairly sensational. Frank Sinatra chartered a special plane and brought Judy Garland, the Bogarts, the Nivens, etc.; then there were Joan Fontaine, Zsa Zsa Gabor, the Joe Cottens, Peter Glenville, Larry Harvey, etc. The noise was terrific. The next day there was a quarter of an hour's radio talk devoted to me in course of which they all lavished paeans of praise on me with the most uninhibited and heart-warming generosity. The Press have been courteous and the photographers insistent but considerate. On Friday I was driven out into the Nevada desert, where I was photographed for *Life* magazine in my dinner-jacket sipping a cup of tea. The temperature was 118°.

(Diary, 12 June 1955)

Much of the material for that fabulous season at Las Vegas had been written, as Coward says, 'very long ago and far away'. But among the new numbers was 'a song about a simple country girl who always kept her eye on the future'.

The climax of Coward's tour de force was his own version of 'Let's Do It'. He first adapted Cole Porter's most famous 'list' song in the Forties and, over the years, the list was always changing. The version which appears here is based on the one published in 1965, which shows remarkable foresight about the House of Commons thirty years later. But one or two wicked lines from Las Vegas have been revived as well.

Alice Is At It Again

Verse 1

In a dear little village remote and obscure
A beautiful maiden resided,
As to whether or not her intentions were pure
Opinion was sharply divided.
She loved to lie out 'neath the darkening sky
And allow the soft breeze to entrance her,
She whispered her dreams to the birds flying by
But seldom received any answer.

Refrain 1

Over the field and along the lane
Gentle Alice would love to stray,
When it came to the end of the day,
She would wander away unheeding,
Dreaming her innocent dreams she strolled
Quite unaffected by heat or cold,
Frequently freckled or soaked with rain,
Alice was out in the lane.
Whom she met there
Every day there
Was a question answered by none,
But she'd get there
And she'd stay there
Till whatever she did was undoubtedly done.
Over the field and along the lane
When her parents had called in vain,
Sadly, sorrowfully, they'd complain,
'Alice is at it again.'

Verse 2

Though that dear little village
Surrounded by trees
Had neither a school nor a college
Gentle Alice acquired from the birds and the bees

240

Some exceedingly practical knowledge.
The curious secrets that nature revealed
She refused to allow to upset her
But she thought when observing the beasts of the field
That things might have been organised better.

Rhythm Refrain

Over the field and along the lane
Gentle Alice would make up
And take up – her stand.
The road was not exactly arterial
But it led to a town near by
Where quite a lot of masculine material
Caught her roving eye.
She was ready to hitchhike
Cadillac or motor-bike,
She wasn't proud or choosey,
All she
Was aiming to be
Was a prinked up,
Minked up
Fly-by-night Floosie.
When old Rajahs
Gave her pearls as large as
Nuts on a chestnut tree
All she said was, 'Fiddlededee,
The wages of sin will be the death of me!'
Over the field and along the lane
Gentle Alice's parents would wait hand in hand.
Her dear old white-headed mother wistfully sipping champagne
Said, 'We've spoiled our child – spared the rod,
Open up the caviare and say Thank God,
We've got no cause to complain,
Alice is at it,
Alice is at it,
Alice is at it again.'

Let's Do It

(With acknowledgements to Cole Porter)

Verse 1

Mr Irving Berlin
Often emphasises sin
In a charming way.
Mr Coward we know
Wrote a song or two to show
Sex was here to stay.
Richard Rodgers it's true
Takes a more romantic view
Of that sly biological urge.
But it really was Cole
Who contrived to make the whole
Thing merge.

Refrain 1

He said that Belgians and Greeks do it,
Nice young men who sell antiques do it,
Let's do it, let's fall in love.
Monkeys whenever you look do it,
Aly Khan and King Farouk do it,
Let's do it, let's fall in love.
Louella Parsons can't quite do it
But she's so highly strung.
Marlene might do it
But she looks far too young.
Each man out there shooting crap does it,
Davy Crockett in that dreadful cap does it,
Let's do it, let's fall in love.

Refrain 2

Our leading writers in swarms do it,
Somerset and all the Maughams do it,
Let's do it, let's fall in love.
The Brontës felt that they must do it,

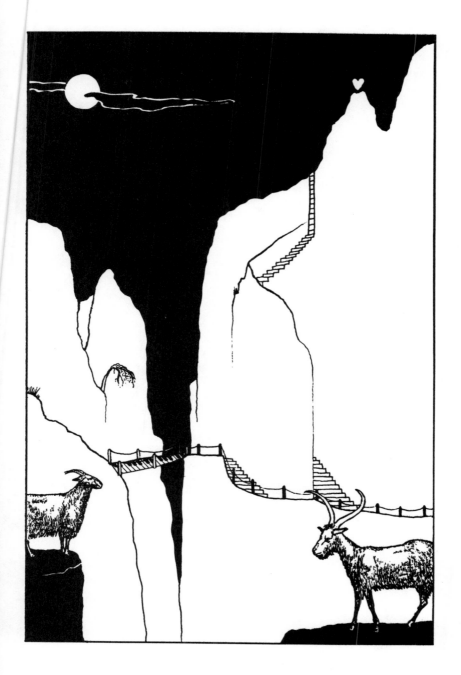

Ernest Hemingway could *just* do it,
Let's do it, let's fall in love.
E. Allan Poe – ho! ho! ho! – did it
But he did it in verse.
H. Beecher Stowe did it
But she had to rehearse.
Tennessee Williams, self-taught, does it,
Kinsey with a deafening Report does it,
Let's do it, let's fall in love.

Verse 2

In the Spring of the year
Inhibitions disappear
And our hearts beat high,
We had better face facts
Every gland that overacts
Has an alibi,
For each bird and each bee,
Each slap-happy sappy tree,
Each temptation that lures us along
Is just Nature elle-même
Merely singing us the same
Old song.

Refrain 3

Girls from the RADA do it,
BBC announcers may do it,
Let's do it, let's fall in love.
The Ballet Jooss to a man do it,
Alfred Lunt and Lynn Fontanne do it,
Let's do it, let's fall in love.
My kith and kin, more or less, do it,
Every uncle and aunt,
But I confess to it,
I've one cousin who can't.
Some mystics, as a routine do it,
Even Evelyn Waugh and Graham Greene do it,
Let's do it, let's fall in love.

243

Refrain 4

The House of Commons en bloc do it,
Civil Servants by the clock do it,
Let's do it, let's fall in love.
Deacons who've done it before do it,
Minor canons with a roar do it,
Let's do it, let's fall in love.
Some rather rorty old rips do it
When they get a bit tight,
Government Whips do it
If it takes them all night,
Old mountain goats in ravines do it,
Probably we'll live to see machines do it,
Let's do it, let's fall in love.

Refrain 5

In Texas some of the men do it,
Others drill a hole and then do it,
Let's do it, let's fall in love.
West Point cadets, forming fours, do it,
People say all those Gabors do it,
Let's do it, let's fall in love.
The most recherché cocottes do it
In a luxury flat,
Locks, Dunns and Scotts do it,
At the drop of a hat.
Each tiny clam you consume does it,
Even Liberace – we assume – does it,
Let's do it, let's fall in love.

The last two lyrics in this section are examples of Coward's prodigality. He could write 'Three Theatrical Dames' for a charity show, careless of the fact that it would probably never be heard again. Similarly, 'Why Must the Show Go On?' was hardly going to join 'There's No Business Like Show Business' or 'Another Opening, Another Show' as one of the anthems of the profession. But how bracing it is to read an acerbic comment on theatrical cliché once in a while.

Three Theatrical Dames

I started from scratch
In a house with a thatch
With two very unpleasant old ladies.
My parents were dead
So I finally fled
And appeared in a tent
Outside Burton-on-Trent
In a very small part in *Quo Vadis*.
I toured in *East Lynne*
And *The Wages of Sin*
Till I couldn't tell one from the other,
Then made a rich friend
And achieved the West End
In a farce called *She Did It For Mother*.

Refrain 1

Three theatrical Dames,
Eminent and respectable,
Our accents are undetectable
And though we've achieved our aims,
If they knew what we'd done
In eighteen ninety-one
They certainly wouldn't have made us Dames.

Verse 2

My very first step
Was Shakespearian 'rep'
Where an awful old 'Ham' used to train us.
I'd nothing to do
In *The Dream* and *The Shrew*
But I carried a spear
In *King John* and *King Lear*
And a hatchet in *Coriolanus*.

I ranted for years
In pavilions on piers
Till my spirits were really at zero,
Then I got a small role
Of a tart with a soul
In a play by Sir Arthur Pinero.

Refrain 2

Three theatrical Dames,
Models of prim propriety,
Accepted by High Society
Because of our famous names,
If they'd asked us to tea
In eighteen ninety-three
They certainly wouldn't have made us Dames.

Verse 3

I made my début
In a canvas canoe
In a horrid American drama.
It wasn't a hit
So I left the 'Legit'
And I got myself backed
In a musical act
Called 'A Night in the Garden of Karma'.
An agent called Klein
Said, 'I'm willing to sign
Whoever that girl who unveils is',
So I got my first chance
With a Biblical dance
In a flop at the Old Prince of Wales's.

Refrain 3

Three theatrical Dames,
Each of our houses we adorn
With photographs of the highly-born
In elegant silver frames,
If they'd caught us in Crewe

In eighteen ninety-two
They certainly wouldn't have made us Dames.

Refrain 4

Three theatrical Dames,
Prominent high and mighty girls,
The fact that we once were flighty girls
Our manner today disclaims,
If they'd seen our high kicks
In eighteen ninety-six
They certainly wouldn't have made us Dames.

Why Must the Show Go On?

Verse 1

The world for some years
Has been sodden with tears
On behalf of the Acting profession.
Each star playing a part
Seems to expect the 'Purple Heart',
It's unorthodox
To be born in a box
But it needn't become an obsession.
Let's hope we have no worse to plague us
Than two shows a night at Las Vegas.
When I think of physicians
And mathematicians
Who don't earn a quarter the dough,
When I look at the faces
Of people in Macy's
There's one thing I'm burning to know:

Refrain 1

Why must the show go on?
It can't be all that indispensable,
To me it really isn't sensible
On the whole

To play a leading role
While fighting those tears you can't control,
Why kick up your legs
When draining the dregs
Of sorrow's bitter cup?
Because you have read
Some idiot has said,
'The curtain must go up!'
I'd like to know why a star takes bows
Having just returned from burying her spouse.
Brave boop-a-doopers,
Go home and dry your tears,
Gallant old troupers,
You've bored us all for years
And when you're so blue,
Wet through
And thoroughly woebegone,
Why must the show go on?
O Mammy!
Why must the show go on?

Verse 2

We're asked to condole
With each tremulous soul
Who steps out to be loudly applauded.
Stars on opening nights
Sob when they see their names in lights.
Though people who act
As a matter of fact
Are financially amply rewarded,
It seems, while pursuing their calling,
Their suffering's simply appalling!
But butchers and bakers
And candlestick makers
Get little applause for their pains
And when I think of miners
And waiters in 'Diners'
One query for ever remains:

248

Refrain 2

Why must the show go on?
The rule is surely not immutable,
It might be wiser and more suitable
Just to close
If you are in the throes
Of personal grief and private woes.
Why stifle a sob
While doing your job
When, if you use your head,
You'd go out and grab
A comfortable cab
And go right home to bed?
Because you're not giving us much fun,
This 'Laugh Clown Laugh' routine's been overdone,
Hats off to Show Folks
For smiling when they're blue
But more comme-il-faut folks
Are sick of smiling through,
And if you're out cold,
Too old
And most of your teeth have gone,
Why must the show go on?
I sometimes wonder
Why must the show go on?

Refrain 3

Why must the show go on?
Why not announce the closing night of it?
The public seem to hate the sight of it,
Dear, and so
Why you should undergo
This terrible strain we'll never know.
We know that you're sad,
We know that you've had
A lot of storm and strife
But is it quite fair

249

To ask us to share
Your dreary private life?
We know you're trapped in a gilded cage
But for Heaven's sake relax and be your age,
Stop being gallant
And don't be such a bore,
Pack up your talent,
There's always plenty more
And if you lose hope
Take dope
And lock yourself in the John,
Why must the show go on?
I'm merely asking
Why must the show go on?

The Sixties

Coward's *1961 musical* Sail Away *had a very complicated genesis. It is distantly derived from his song 'A Bar on the Piccola Marina' and was originally conceived as a film about Mrs Wentworth-Brewster 'who discovered in the nick of time that life was for living'. It eventually emerged as a stage musical about Mimi Paragon, a cruise director in charge of a group of American tourists in Europe. Mimi was played both in New York and London by Elaine Stritch, who regularly brought the house down – or tore the place up – with this definitive number about foreign language phrase-books.*

Useless Useful Phrases

When the tower of Babel fell
It caused a lot of unnecessary Hell.
Personal 'rapport'
Became a complicated bore
And a lot more difficult than it had been before,
When the tower of Babel fell.

The Chinks and the Japs
And the Finns and Lapps
Were reduced to a helpless stammer,
And the ancient Greeks
Took at least six weeks
To learn their Latin grammar.
The guttural wheeze
Of the Portuguese
Filled the brains of the Danes
With horror,
And verbs, not lust,
Caused the final bust
In Sodom and Gomorrah.

If it hadn't been for that
Bloody building falling flat
I would not have had to learn Italiano
And keep muttering 'Si, si'
And 'Mi Chiamano Mimi'
Like an ageing Metropolitan soprano!

I should not have had to look
At that ghastly little book
Till my brain becomes as soft as mayonnaise is,
Messrs Hugo and Berlitz
Must have torn themselves to bits
Dreaming up so many useless useful phrases.

Refrain 1

Pray tell me the time,
It is six,
It is seven,
It's half past eleven,
It's twenty to two,
I want thirteen stamps,
Does your child have convulsions?
Please bring me some rhubarb,
I need a shampoo,
How much is that hat?
I desire some red stockings,
My mother is married,
These boots are too small,
My aunt has a cold,
Shall we go to the opera?
This meat is disgusting,
Is this the town hall?

Refrain 2

My cousin is deaf,
Kindly bring me a hatchet,
Pray pass me the pepper,
What pretty cretonne,

What time is the train?
It is late,
It is early,
It's running on schedule,
It's here,
It has gone.
I've written six letters,
I've written no letters,
Pray fetch me a horse,
I have need of a groom,
This isn't my passport,
This isn't my hatbox,
Please show me the way
To Napoleon's tomb.

Refrain 3

The weather is cooler,
The weather is hotter,
Pray fasten my corsets,
Please bring me my cloak,
I've lost my umbrella,
I'm in a great hurry,
I'm going,
I'm staying,
D'you mind if I smoke?
This mutton is tough,
There's a mouse in my bedroom,
This egg is delicious,
This soup is too thick,
Please bring me a trout,
What an excellent pudding,
Pray hand me my gloves,
I'm going to be sick!

The last substantial piece in this collection is one of the least well known. Yet it makes a fitting keystone because it celebrates the people and the country which Coward knew so well and the values which he always stood for: loyalty, courage and good manners.

Not Yet the Dodo

In the countryside of England
Tucked snugly beneath the Sussex Downs
Or perhaps a mile or two away
From gentle cathedral towns
There still exist today
A diminishing few
A residue
Of unregenerate characters who
Despite two wars and the Welfare State
And incomes sadly inadequate
Still, summoned by Sunday morning chimes,
Walk briskly to church to say their prayers
And later, in faded chintz armchairs,
Read of divorces, wars and crimes
And, shocked by the trend of world affairs,
Compose,
In a cosy, post-prandial doze,
Tart letters of protest to *The Times*.
These people still tap the weather-glass
And prune their roses and mow their grass
Representative
For so long as they live
Of the English upper middle-class.

General and Lady Bedrington
Lived on the borders of Cornwall and Devon
In a red-brick, weather-bleached Georgian house
With a distant view of the sea,
They drove into Plymouth twice a week
In an ancient Austin Seven
And in summer, on rather a sloping lawn,
Played croquet after tea,
The thirty years of their married life
Had been lived in far away places,
Before and during and after the war
They'd always been on the move.

Alien climates and tropical suns
Had sallowed their English faces
And now, at long last, their elderly ways
Were set in a tranquil groove.
The household staff which should have been six
Was reduced to one and a 'daily'.
The 'one' was Maggie Macdonald
Who'd been Lady Bedrington's maid
In the early, hurly-burly days
When they'd settled themselves so gaily
In that 'barracky' house in the compound
Of the Garrison at Port Said.
Later, when Priscilla was born
And so sadly and swiftly died,
It was Maggie who coped with everything,
Efficient beyond belief.
It was Maggie who, in the desolate hours,
Stayed by her mistress' side
And with dour, stubborn Scottish sense
Blunted the edges of grief.

It was Maggie also who, some years after,
When Barry was born in Delhi,
Nursed Lady B. through the merciless heat
And ultimately contrived,
On a breathless morning at six o'clock,
While the bugles were sounding Reveille,
To deliver the baby an hour and a half
Before the doctor arrived.

And later still, when war had come,
She brought the boy home to his Granny
In a crowded troopship that sailed for England
Under a brazen sky.
She fluttered a handkerchief from the deck,
Proud of her role as a 'Nanny',
While Lady Bedrington, blinded with tears,
Waved the convoy 'goodbye'.

Maggie Macdonald was old and grey
But far from full of sleep
She had rheumatism in hip and knee
And her eyes were not what they used to be
But she woke with the morning every day
As though she'd a tryst to keep.

She ran the house like an oiled machine,
She did the marketing, cooked the meals:
On afternoons off, in her Sunday black
She walked three miles to the village and back
With a vast, asthmatical Aberdeen
Lumbering at her heels.

Maggie saw no indignity
In the fact that she worked for others.
She returned to Scotland once a year
For a fortnight's family atmosphere
In a little grey house outside Dundee
With one of her married brothers.

There were lots of relatives, brusque but kind;
Grandnephews and nieces to see
She brought them presents and gave them treats
And walked with them through the Dundee streets
But always, at the back of her mind,
Were the General and Lady B.

But even more than the Bedringtons
It was Barry who claimed her heart,
She wept each time he left for school,
Upbraiding herself for a doting fool
And stuffed him with cream and saffron buns
And apple and blackberry tart.

And when, as an undergraduate,
He came home for long weekends,

She washed his shirts and pressed his slacks
And lied for him and covered his tracks
And was ready with soda-bicarbonate
For him and his Oxford friends.

The problem of Barry's future career
Blew up at his coming-of-age.
He chose his moment and seized his chance
And, in the library after the dance
Announced, in a voice quite firm and clear,
That he meant to go on the stage.

The General went purple in the face,
Lady Bedrington kept her head.
They both of them tried to talk him round
But the boy inflexibly held his ground
Until at last, with unhappy grace,
They surrendered and went to bed.

Maggie was told the news the next day
And felt she might easily faint
But she pursed her lips and packed his bags,
Gloomily tied on the luggage tags
And waved the pride of her life away
To his world of powder and paint.

General and Lady Bedrington
With inward excitement but outward calm
Arrived, as usual, at Paddington
Where Barry was waiting, efficient and kind,
Though the General noticed, with vague alarm,
That his hair was rather too long behind.
With him was standing a tall young man
Wearing corduroys and an open sweater
Who, Barry explained, was Danny Hoag
With whom he was sharing a two-room flat
In a cul-de-sac off the Earl's Court Road.
He added, impressively, that Dan

257

Quite frequently drew designs for *Vogue*
And Lady B., with a private sigh,
Ardently wished she could like him better.
Barry procured a cab outside
And off they drove through the London rain,
Danny dripping with Irish charm,
Caressing them with his gentle brogue,
Barry, voluble, chatting away,
Telling them with self-conscious pride,
About the theatre, about the play,
About some pompous old Blimp who wrote
Explosively to the *Telegraph*
Protesting against the author's use
Of four-letter words and his abuse
Of England's quality, England's pride
England's achievements past and present.
The General stared at the street outside
And thought the play sounded damned unpleasant.

When they had reached the De Glenn Hotel
And the boys had taken the taxi on,
General and Lady Bedrington,
After their welcome from the staff,
Walked upstairs to their double room
Both thinking thoughts best left unsaid
Both of them trying valiantly,
Sitting together on the bed,
To help each other to vanquish gloom.
'I didn't think much of that Irish bloke!'
The General murmured unhappily.
His wife, as though he had made a joke,
Laughed indulgently, patted his knee
And telephoned down to order tea.

They went to the theatre
Sat through the play
And were shocked, bewildered and bored,
And, during the final curtain calls,

Numb, in their complimentary stalls,
They looked at each other, looked away
And forced themselves to applaud.

The audience straggled up the aisle
And vanished into the mews
But both the General and Lady B.,
Frozen in hopeless apathy
Sat on in silence for a while
Like people who've had bad news.

Stunned, inarticulate and deeply tired
They finally were led resignedly
Up four steep steps and through an iron door
To meet the cast and author of the play.
The odd young woman who escorted them
Wore, with a skin-tight jumper, denim slacks,
Black stockings, grubby plimsolls and a beret
From under which curtains of greasy hair
Descended to her shoulders. On the stage
Barry received them and presenting them
With filial pride and touching eagerness,
To all his strange colleagues who stood around
Proudly upon their consecrated ground.
Poor Lady Bedrington, with social grace,
Managed to conquer her embarrassment
And murmer some polite but empty phrases.
The General, mute before his only son,
Finally cleared his throat and said, 'Well done!'

The supper party after the play
In Barry and Danny's flat
Could not be accurately called
An unqualified success.
The cast were all invited
And some other cronies appeared
Including a sibilant gentleman
In velvet slacks and a beard

259

And a sullen Lesbian in evening dress
Who brought a Siamese cat.

General and Lady B. were received
With cautious politesse.
A tall girl offered them sandwiches
And a whisky and soda each.
They sat on a sofa side by side
And longed to be home in bed.
There was little ham in the sandwiches
And a great deal too much bread
But they chewed them bravely, bereft of speech,
Encased in self-consciousness.

The party, after an hour or two,
Abandoned its formal endeavour.
A sallow youth with enormous ears
Was coaxed to do imitations.
The people he mimic'd obviously
Were known to everyone there
But the Bedringtons rather missed the point
For they didn't know who they were
And Barry's hissed explanations
Bewildered them more than ever.

A girl with slightly projecting teeth
Agreed, after much persuasion,
To tell the story of how she'd been
Seduced in 'digs' in Hull.
The present company evidently
Had heard it often before
And when she'd finished, vociferously,
Demanded an encore
To which she at once assented.
And told an equally dull,
Long, complicated anecdote
Which was even more Rabelaisian.

The Bedringtons, over their married years,
Had learned to accept defeats.
So, at the same moment, they both got up
Still smiling with frozen eyes.
A hush descended upon the group
While politenesses were said
And Lady Bedrington's cloak was fetched
From Barry and Danny's bed.
Barry got them a taxi
And, muttering swift 'goodbyes'
They drove back to the De Glenn Hotel
Through the bright, deserted streets.
That night they lay, restless, in their thin twin beds
And Lady B. discreetly wept a little.
The General, equally wretched, bravely tried
To reassure her, soothe her with platitudes.
'Youth will be served,' he said. 'We can't expect
Old heads on young shoulders, this is a passing phase,
He'll soon grow out of it. Cheer up my dear,
It's dangerous to take up moral attitudes.
Let the young idiot and his ghastly friends
Enjoy themselves and go their foolish ways.'
He got out of his bed to kiss her cheek
As he had done for nearly forty years.
'Silly old thing,' she said, and dried her tears.
The General, having got back to bed,
Switched off the light and, turning on his side,
Tried, unsuccessfully to sleep.
Lady B. also, in the oppressive dark,
Waited unhopefully for oblivion.
Again, entirely soundlessly, she wept
Again it was almost dawn before they slept.

To royal garden parties every year
Vast numbers of loyal subjects are invited.
From South and West and East and North they come,
Some from the country, some from the suburbs, some
(On leave from Zanzibar or the Seychelles)

From inexpensive Kensington hotels.
Matriarchs in large hats and flowered prints,
Ebony delegates from far Dominions,
One or two sharp-eyed ladies from the Press,
Tiny green gentlemen in native dress,
Colonial governors with eager wives
Jostling in line for when the Queen arrives.
Bright débutantes quite recently presented,
Actresses of impeccable repute,
A novelist or two, bishops galore,
Plus members of the diplomatic corps,
A smattering of ancient admirals
And matrons from the London hospitals.
Cabinet ministers, some rural deans,
Newly created knights and peers and dames,
Field-marshals, air marshals, a few VCs.
Sauntering beneath the royal trees
Every mutation of the middle-class
Proudly parading on the royal grass.

The Queen, surrounded by her retinue,
Graciously moves among her varied guests.
Curtseys are made, heads are correctly bowed
And as she makes her progress through the crowd
Pauses are organised for conversation
With those marked on the list for presentation.
Following her, forming their separate groups,
Some other members of the royal family,
Sharing with affable, polite mobility,
Part of the afternoon's responsibility.
After an hour or so of this routine,
Either in blazing sun or gentle rain,
The royalties, by mutual consent,
Withdraw themselves to an exclusive tent,
Weary of bobbing head and bended knee,
And thankfully sit down to have their tea.

The porter at the De Glenn Hotel
Having procured a hired limousine,
Stood to attention as the Bedringtons
Set proudly forth to keep their regal tryst.
The General, in top hat and morning-coat,
Lady B., in a floating chiffon dress,
Climbed with unhurried calm into the car
Though Lady B.'s enormous cartwheel hat
Needed to be manoeuvred with some care.
Walter, the valet, Rose, the chambermaid,
Ernest, the waiter on the second floor,
Waved from the landing window, while Miss Holt,
Her pince-nez glinting in the morning sun,
Forsook the cashier's desk and with a cry,
Rushed down the hotel steps to say 'goodbye'.

We British are a peculiar breed
Undemonstrative on the whole.
It takes a very big shock indeed
To dent our maddening self-control.

The slow decline of our Island Race
Alien prophets have long foreseen,
But still, to symbolise English grace,
We go to London to see the Queen.

Our far-flung Empire imposed new rules
And lasted a century or so
Until, engrossed with our football pools
We shrugged our shoulders and let it go.

But old traditions are hard to kill
However battered about they've been.
And it's still, for some, an authentic thrill
To go to London to see the Queen.

The car moved very slowly through the traffic.
Its occupants sat still, preserving elegance,

The General would like to have crossed his legs
And smoked a cigarette, but he refrained;
His trousers were well-pressed and must remain
Well-pressed until he got back home again.

Sense of Occasion and the Royal Touch
Wakened in their reactionary hearts
Old memories of less disturbing years
When social values were more specified.
Before the proletariat, en masse,
Reversed the status of the ruling class.

For them the afternoon (until the end)
Was beautiful and somehow reassuring.
They saw the Queen pass by and Lady B.
Executed a most successful curtsey:
Then the Queen Mother, with her lovely smile,
Chatted to them both for quite a while.

Past friends appeared, perhaps a little changed:
Emily Blake who'd made that awful scene
With Boy Macfadden on the polo ground;
Both of the Granger girls, now safely married,
Isabel Pratt, whose face had grown much larger,
Still with her rather dubious Maharajah.

The Hodgsons, alas, in mourning for poor Hilda;
Vernon and Hattie Phillips from Madras,
Everyone welcoming, everyone pleased to see them,
But typically it was Ella Graves
Wearing a hideous hat and sharp with malice,
Who pounced upon them as they left the Palace.

Eleanor Graves, née Eleanor Walker,
Had always been a compulsive talker,
A fact
Which, combined with her monumental lack of tact,
Caused quite a lot of people to avoid her.

This might conceivably have annoyed her
Very much indeed
If she'd
Possessed enough humility to perceive it,
Or believe it,
But Oh, no – Oh, dear me no!
Her sense of superiority was so
Deeply ingrained
That she remained
Garrulous, mischievous and indiscreet,
Blandly protected by her own conceit.
'I'd no idea you were here!' she shrieked,
Inserting herself between them,
And 'It seemed like centuries,' she wailed,
Since the last time she'd seen them.
She said they *must* see her sweet new flat,
'Just pop in for drinks, or dine'
And added, with shrill irrelevance,
That Lady B.'s hat was divine.
They were trapped there, waiting for their car
Without a hope of escape.
The General wished she could be tied up
And gagged with adhesive tape.
It wasn't until they'd both agreed
To lunch on the following day
That at long last their car appeared
And they thankfully drove away.

It was after lunch on the next unhappy day,
When her other guests had said their 'goodbyes' and left,
That Eleanor, insufferably mysterious,
Seized on the moment she'd been waiting for.
'There's something I just must warn you about,' she hissed,
'And if you weren't such old and valued friends,
I wouldn't interfere or say a word,
But as I'm so fond of you and this is serious,
I thought I'd take my courage in both hands
And tell you, straight from the shoulder, what I've heard

About your Barry and that Irish character
Who, judging from all accounts, are quite inseparable.
As yet the situation's not irreparable,
But action must be taken, something done,
To salvage the reputation of your son.'

The General's eyes became cold and bleak.
He set his jaw and his face was grim.
He opened his mouth, prepared to speak,
But Lady B. was too quick for him.
She rose to her feet and swiftly turned
With smiling lips and a heart of lead.
'How kind of you to be so concerned,
We're both devoted to Dan,' she said.

On leaving Eleanor's flat they took a bus
And sat in silence, worried and unhappy.
They left the bus at Prince's Gate and walked
Into the Park, still without speaking, still
Struggling to evade the implications
Of Eleanor's malign insinuations.

Sitting on two green chairs beneath the trees
They absently surveyed the London pastoral:
Nurses and children, governesses, dogs,
Two lovers sleeping in each other's arms,
A young man with his coloured shirt undone
Profiting from the unexpected sun.

Mutely they realised that here and now
It was essential for them both to face
Some of the facts of life which, hitherto,
Their inbred reticence had stowed away,
With other fixed taboos of various kinds,
Down in the depths of their subconscious minds.

Their self-protective innocence of course
Was not as valid as it seemed to be.

They both of them, within their private thoughts,
Knew things that neither of them would admit.
Lady B. traced patterns on the ground,
With her umbrella-tip. The General frowned.

Sitting there quietly on their painted chairs
Aware that they were together, yet alone,
They watched, without noticing, the changing scene:
The brilliant sunlight of the afternoon
Softening and merging into early evening
The shadows lengthening under the London trees,
Staining with grey the brownish, trodden grass.
The summer noises seemed to be changing too,
Becoming less strident as the day wore on:
The hum of traffic, buses grinding gears,
Children's shrill voices, sharp staccato barks
From those alert, exclusively London dogs
Which seem indigenous to London Parks.
Finally, stiffly, they got up and walked,
Still without speaking, back to the hotel.
In both their minds decisions had been made,
Mutually arrived at, without discussion,
And when they reached their bedroom Lady B.
Took off her hat, stared in the looking-glass
And searched her face with anxious scrutiny
Discovering with relief that all the strains
And inward conflicts of the last few hours
Had left no outward traces to betray her.
Her eyes perhaps did look a trifle tired
But then, all things considered, that was not
Entirely to be wondered at. She sat
Decisively upon the bed and took
The telephone receiver from its hook.

Barry and Danny got back to the flat at six
After a rather aimless afternoon
Searching for antiques in the Brompton Road.
Barry was hot, irritable, conscious of guilt,

Because he hadn't made the slightest effort
To find out if his parents were all right
And if their glum little Kensington hotel
Was comfortable. He could have sent some flowers
If he had thought of it. He mooched about,
Took off his clothes and flung himself on the bed.
Danny looked at him quizzically and said,
'Why don't we call your rather frightening mother
And ask them both to dine somewhere or other?'

The telephone, at that moment, rang.
Barry lifted it to his ear
And suffered a further guilty pang
When his mother's voice said, 'Is that you, dear?'
At any rate the evening went off well.
The Bedringtons were fetched from their hotel,
Squeezed into Danny's second-hand MG
And driven, perhaps a thought erratically,
To dine in a converted Wesleyan chapel
Called, rather whimsically, 'The Golden Apple'.

The room was tiny, lit by flickering candles.
The waiters wore canvas trousers, vests and sandals,
The menus, although very large indeed,
The General found difficult to read,
Poor Lady B. in her self-conscious flurry
Rather unwisely plumped for chicken curry.

The noise was deafening, the service, slow.
Danny, resolved to make the party go,
Laid himself out, with Irish charm and wit,
To loosen up the atmosphere a bit.
And Lady B. was vaguely mortified
To see the General laugh until he cried.

Later that evening, General and Lady B.,
Preoccupied with their eventful day,
Slowly prepared themselves to face the night.

Lady B. pensively took off her rings
And put them in the dressing-table drawer.
The General went stumping down the passage
As usual, to the bathroom, with his sponge-bag.
Lady B. rubbing her face with cleansing cream,
Could hear him in the distance, gargling.
Suddenly she remembered Ella's words:
Her bland, unwarranted impertinence,
'That Irish character', 'Something must be done
To save the reputation of your son!'
Lady B., conscious that her hands were shaking,
Made a tremendous effort at control
And, with a slight, contemptuous grimace,
Finally continued massaging her face.

On the fourth day of their dejected holiday,
Breakfasting in the hotel dining-room,
General and Lady B. without discussion,
Inspired by age-old mutual telepathy,
Arrived at the same conclusion. Lady B.
Absently took some toast, then put it back.
'I think', she said, 'I'll go upstairs and pack.'

It was Danny who answered the telephone,
Barry was still asleep.
Lady B.'s voice was icily polite,
'I really must apologise', she said,
'For calling you so early in the morning.
I'd like to have a few words with my son.
However if he isn't yet awake
Please don't disturb him – You could perhaps explain,
We've had a tiresome telegram from home
Which means that we must leave immediately
And so we are leaving on the midday train.'
Danny, completely taken by surprise,
Tried, unsuccessfully, to sound dismayed
But Lady B. cut short his protestations
Quite firmly, still implacably polite.

'Please tell him', she went on, 'that we will write
The moment we get back. It *was* such fun',
She added, 'dining with you both
At that strange restaurant the other night.'

Maggie Macdonald had second sight
A loving, instinctive flair.
The telegram Lady B. had sent
Confirmed her growing presentiment
That trouble was in the air.

She waited grimly to meet the train
Though her welcoming smile was gay
And while they greeted her normally
And chatted away informally
She searched their faces for signs of strain
And the signs were as clear as day.

At dinner, outwardly serene,
The General praised the salmon.
Afterwards he and Lady B.
Sat for a while and watched TV
Then, gallantly loyal to routine,
Played three games of backgammon.

Maggie, knowing her mistress very well
Was certain she would not go up to bed
Without some hint, some sort of explanation
Of why they had so suddenly returned.
So, busying herself with little chores,
She put the cat out, tidied the dresser drawers,
Ironed some handkerchiefs and wound the clock,
Pottered about, arranged the breakfast tray,
Put on the kettle for a cup of tea
And finally, with nothing else to do,
She sat down in her creaking cane armchair
And waited for a footstep on the stair.
She heard the front door slam and knew the General,

Had gone out for his customary stroll;
Silence enclosed the house, silence so deep
That the bland ticking of the kitchen clock
Sounded presumptuous, a loud intrusion,
Confusing more her heart's dismayed confusion.
Edward miaowed outside, she let him in
And, stalking before her like a conqueror,
He jumped into his basket, washed his face,
Shot her a glance and delicately yawned.
She gently massaged him behind the ears
And, unaccountably, burst into tears.

Of course, at this moment, Lady B. appeared
Catching poor Maggie red-eyed and betrayed.
She paused for a moment at the door and then
Swiftly advanced and took her in her arms.
'Don't, Maggie dear, please please don't cry,' she said,
'It isn't all that bad, really it's not.
Nothing appalling's happened, nothing sad,
Merely a tiresomeness, let's just sit down
Quite calmly and discuss it, you and me,
And, while we're at it, have a cup of tea.'

They sat there in close conference
With their crowded years behind them
Both bewildered and both distressed
But both determined to do their best
Not to allow their innocence
And prejudices to blind them.

They both knew more and they both knew less
Than either of them admitted.
To them, the infinite, complex
And strange divergencies of sex
Were based on moral capriciousness
And less to be blamed than pitied.

They both agreed that there'd always seemed
A 'difference' about Barry.
He'd never plagued them with sudden scares
Involving dubious love affairs;
Preserving himself, so they fondly dreamed,
For the girl he would finally marry.

But here they were guilty of sophistry
For, with deep, unspoken dread,
Their minds rejected the ghastly day
That would whisk their paragon away
Beyond their possessive idolatry
To an alien marriage bed.

Their earlier fears having been replaced
By faintly embarrassed relief,
They tried, with mutual urgency,
To cope with this new emergency;
Like storm-tossed mariners suddenly faced
With a strange, uncharted reef.

For more than three hours they sat there in the kitchen.
Maggie made sandwiches and brewed fresh tea.
Out in the quiet night the world was sleeping
Lulled by the murmur of the distant sea.
Finally Maggie, with shrewd common sense,
Embarked upon her speech for the defence.

'If you want my opinion,' she said, 'I think
We're both of us wasting our breath.
You can't judge people by rule of thumb
And if we sit gabbling till Kingdom Come
We'll neither of us sleep a wink
And worry ourselves to death.
People are made the way they're made
And it isn't anyone's fault.
Nobody's taste can quite agree,
Some like coffee and some like tea

And Guinness rather than lemonade
And pepper rather than salt.

'If Mr Barry had got caught out
By some little teenage whore
And brought her home as his blushing bride
Not only would we be mortified,
But we'd have a real problem to fuss about
And worry a great deal more.

'Being a "spinster" as you might say
Not overburdened with looks,
I never went in for much romance,
Though I had some fun when I got the chance,
And whatever knowledge has come my way
Has come through people and books.

'I don't know what this is all about
But Barry's the one I care for.
I don't mind whether he's strange or not
Or goes to bed with a Hottentot.
It's not good us trying to puzzle out
The what, the why and the wherefore.'

When Maggie's tirade came to an end
She suddenly bowed her head.
Lady B. rose and kissed her cheek
And, when she could trust herself to speak
Said 'Now, my most loyal and loving friend
It's time we went up to bed.'

During the next few days the weather held.
The russet Devon cliffs cast purple shadows
Staining the edges of the quiet sea.
The General played golf, Lady B. pottered
About the garden, old Mrs Macklehenny
Drove out from Saltash with her married niece,
Ate a vast luncheon and remained for tea,

273

On the fifth morning Lady B. sat down
Purposefully at her writing-desk,
Unscrewed her fountain-pen, stared at the view,
Absently noting an old cargo ship
Lumbering across the shining bay.
The dark smoke from its funnel twisting high
Scribbled a question mark against the sky.
'My darling boy,' she wrote. 'You really must
Forgive me for not writing days ago
To thank you for our little jaunt to Town.
You can't imagine how Papa and I
Enjoyed ourselves, you really were so sweet
To give your aged parents such a treat.
The weather here is perfect, not a cloud.
You'd almost think you were in Italy.
The garden's drying up of course, no rain
For nearly two whole weeks. Old Mr Drew,
The one who used to help you with your stamps,
Suddenly died last Saturday, so sad
But still, all things considered, a release,
When one is ninety-four one can't complain
At ceasing upon the midnight with no pain.
The Hilliard girls are back from Switzerland
Looking, Papa says, commoner than ever.
Hilda, the one who's said to be so clever,
Met some professor in the Engadine
And got engaged to him all in a minute!
And he's apparently quite mad and drinks –
Perhaps she's not so clever as she thinks.
That's all my news and so I'd better stop
And not go rambling on like poor Aunt Jane
Who, incidentally, fell down again
Just outside Gorringe's, the poor old duck
Seems to be really haunted by bad luck.'
Lady B. paused, and, nibbling her pen,
Frowned for a moment and then wrote 'P.S.
Please give our love to Danny and remember
That we expect you *both* in mid-September.'

General and Lady Bedrington
Lived on the borders of Cornwall and Devon
In a red-brick, weather-bleached Georgian house
With its distant view of the sea.
They still drove to Plymouth twice a week
In their rattling Austin Seven
And still, if the weather was feasible,
Played croquet after tea.

Maggie still tramped to the village
With Black Angus, the Aberdeen.
The sun still rose and the sun still set
And the Eddystone light still shone.
Lady B. and the General both
Encased in their daily routine
Began insensibly to forget
Their excursion to Babylon.

In November, 1972, there was an evening of famous faces at Claridge's to honour Noël, with literati and glitterati en masse. In the middle of it, Noël was the most controlled person present, calmly smoking his cigarettes and putting on a performance worthy of a proscenium setting. The inevitable piano was played by Burt Bacharach, Alan Jay Lerner and Frederick Loewe.

A hush fell on the room as Noël started to rise. Coley and I reached to help him but he was determined to manage on his own. Everyone in that room took each faltering step with him until he reached the piano stool and, with Larry's help, sat down. There was no doubt in my mind he'd manage, that nothing would prevent this final show. Everyone there instinctively knew that this was the last time they'd ever see him perform.

He looked down at his hands on the keys. What thoughts were going through his mind? The child actor holding his mother's hand and listening to the sound of the curtain going up? The glory years when the words and music used him like a conduit? Gertie? Las Vegas? After all the ups and downs, it had ended in a way that he'd never have dared to write!

He picked out a few tentative chords and the whole room breathed again. In that thin little voice, now almost a whisper, Noël took them back forty-three years with a song which seemed to sum up an entire lifetime:

. . . I think if only—
Somebody splendid really needed me,
Someone affectionate and dear,
Cares would be ended if I knew that she
Wanted to have me near.
But I believe that since my life began
The most I've had is just
A talent to amuse.
Heigho, if love were all!

A small smile playing about his lips, Noël made to get up. Emotion flowed through the room, embracing us all. Twenty years later I can still feel that frail body trembling as he allowed us to take him back to his table.

But that smile was the smile of the boy actor, hearing his first applause.

In 1973 Coward arranged for the manuscript of a short poem to be auctioned in aid of the Actors' Fund of America. He died in March of that year and Laurence Olivier read this last piece at the Service of Thanksgiving for Noël Coward's life in St Martin-in-the-Fields.

When I Have Fears

When I have fears, as Keats had fears,
Of the moment I'll cease to be,
I console myself with vanished years,
Remembered laughter, remembered tears,
And the peace of the changing sea.

When I feel sad, as Keats felt sad,
That my life is so nearly done,
It gives me comfort to dwell upon
Remembered friends who are dead and gone
And the jokes we had and the fun.

How happy they are I cannot know,
But happy am I who loved them so.